US

TEXTBOOKS IN MATHEMATICS

EDITED BY

R. D. CARMICHAEL

PROFESSOR OF MATHEMATICS, UNIVERSITY OF ILLINOIS

BRIEF
ANALYTIC GEOMETRY

By

THOMAS E. MASON

Professor of Mathematics, Purdue University

and

CLIFTON T. HAZARD

Associate Professor of Mathematics, Purdue University

GINN AND COMPANY
BOSTON · NEW YORK · CHICAGO · LONDON
ATLANTA · DALLAS · COLUMBUS · SAN FRANCISCO

The Athenæum Press

GINN AND COMPANY · PRO-
PRIETORS · BOSTON · U.S.A.

PREFACE

This book is an abridgment of the authors' Analytic Geometry. In this edition the subject matter has been adapted to a schedule of fifty to sixty lessons. The experience of the authors leads them to believe that such a course provides an adequate preparation for the study of the calculus as well as a good introduction to the methods of analytic geometry. This text aims to avoid the confusion and discouragement which many students experience when considerable portions of a text are omitted from the class assignments.

The chapter on Tangents, Normals, Diameters, Poles, and Polars and the chapter on Empirical Equations, which appear in the larger book, are omitted entirely in this brief course.

In order to save time, the treatment of polar coördinates has been concentrated into a single chapter instead of being treated simultaneously with rectangular coördinates in the development of the course.

Several omissions have been made which affect only parts of chapters. In a few instances more illustrative material has been added where it seemed that it would be helpful to the student.

The chief departure from the usual order of presentation of the topics of analytic geometry is that of placing the chapter on the straight line ahead of the chapter on the general problem of equation and locus, as is done also in the larger edition. The authors have found in their classroom experience that students retain from their work in elementary algebra some knowledge of the relation between locus and equation in the case of the straight line. This furnishes a starting point for the systematic treatment of the straight line. Thus the student comes to the general correspondence between equations and geometric loci with better preparation to comprehend it.

While many of the exercises of the larger edition have been retained, more than half are new. The exercises, as well as the text, are designed to develop methods of investigation rather than to teach specific properties of certain curves and surfaces. The exercises are numerous and varied, and it is not likely that any class will attempt all of them. The large number of exercises will allow the teacher a wide choice, varying from simple drill problems to problems that will interest his best students.

Our appreciation is expressed to our colleagues who have helped us with their suggestions and constructive criticisms.

T. E. M.
C. T. H.

PURDUE UNIVERSITY

CONTENTS

PLANE ANALYTIC GEOMETRY

CHAPTER I. THE POINT

CHAPTER III. EQUATION AND LOCUS

CHAPTER IV. THE CIRCLE

CHAPTER V. OTHER SECOND DEGREE CURVES

THE PARABOLA

THE ELLIPSE

The Hyperbola

Conics

CHAPTER VI. OTHER TYPES OF CURVES IN RECTANGULAR COÖRDINATES

Algebraic Curves

Transcendental Curves

CHAPTER X. SURFACES AND CURVES

BRIEF ANALYTIC GEOMETRY

n sides and altitudes parallel to the axes. Or the tri-
le may be inclosed in a rectangle with sides parallel to
axes and the required area found by subtracting the

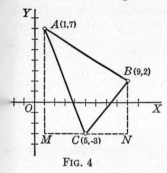

FIG. 4

areas of right triangles from
the area of the rectangle. The
following example illustrates
the use of a trapezoid and
triangles.

EXAMPLE. Find the area of
the triangle whose vertices are
$A(1, 7)$, $B(9, 2)$, and $C(5, -3)$.

Draw through the vertices
of the triangle the auxiliary
lines MN, AM, and BN, as

own in the figure and observe that the coördinates of the
ints M and N are $(1, -3)$ and $(9, -3)$, respectively. Then

ea $\triangle ABC$ = area trapezoid $AMNB$

$$- \text{area } \triangle AMC - \text{area } \triangle BNC$$

$$= \frac{MA + NB}{2} \cdot MN - \frac{MA \cdot MC}{2} - \frac{CN \cdot NB}{2}$$

$$= \frac{10 + 5}{2} \cdot 8 - \frac{10 \cdot 4}{2} - \frac{4 \cdot 5}{2} = 30.$$

The area of any polygon may be found in a similar manner.

EXERCISES

1. Plot the following points:

$_1(2, 3)$; $P_3(-3, 5)$; $P_5(7, 0)$; $P_7(-5, 0)$;
$_2(4, -1)$; $P_4(-6, -2)$; $P_6(0, -4)$; $P_8(0, 0)$.

2. Plot the following points on the same diagram: $(-4, 3)$;
$-2, 2\frac{1}{2})$; $(0, 2)$; $(2, \frac{3}{2})$; $(4, 1)$; $(8, 0)$; $(10, -\frac{1}{2})$; and $(12, -1)$.
hat apparent characteristic does this set of points possess?

3. Plot the following points and connect them by a smooth
urve in the order of increasing abscissas: $(-4, -6.6)$; $(-3, 0)$;
$(-2, 3)$; $(-1, 3.6)$; $(0, 3)$; $(1, 2.4)$; $(2, 3)$; $(2.5, 3.9)$; and $(3, 6)$.
Would the shape of the curve be materially changed if the points
$(-1, 3.6)$ and $(1, 2.4)$ were omitted?

PLANE ANALYTIC GEOMETRY

CHAPTER I

THE POINT

1. Definition. Analytic geometry is a branch of mathematics in which one studies geometry by means of algebra.
A correspondence is set up between a geometric locus and
one or more equations, and properties of the locus are determined from the equations. In order to connect algebra and
geometry use is made of a coördinate system which furnishes
a means for locating points in a plane or in space.

2. Rectangular coördinates. In the coördinate system employed most frequently two straight lines intersecting at right
angles* are used as lines of ref-
erence. A point is located in
the plane of these lines by giving its perpendicular distance
and direction from each of
them. The distances with signs
indicating directions are called
the **coördinates** of the point.
The lines from which distances
are measured are called the
axes of coördinates, or briefly

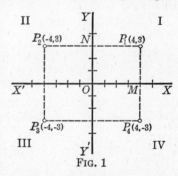

FIG. 1

axes. The point of intersection of the axes is called the **origin**
of coördinates, or the **origin**. In Fig. 1 the line XOX' is

---

* Two lines not at right angles may be used, but the resulting algebra is, in
general, more complicated than in the case of lines at right angles. Any system
of coördinates using two intersecting lines as axes is called Cartesian after Réne
Descartes (1596–1650), a French mathematician.

called the *x*-axis, and the line YOY' is called the *y*-axis. Distances measured to the right of the *y*-axis are usually called positive and those measured to the left negative. Distances measured upward from the *x*-axis are usually called positive and those measured downward negative. The choice of positive direction is a matter of convenience and may change from problem to problem.

That coördinate which indicates the distance of a point to the right or to the left of the *y*-axis is called the **abscissa**, or **x-coördinate** of the point; and that coördinate which indicates the distance above or below the *x*-axis is called the **ordinate**, or the **y-coördinate** of the point. The position of a point is indicated by writing its coördinates in a parenthesis, thus: (abscissa, ordinate). For example, the point P_1 in Fig. 1 is (NP_1, MP_1), or $(4, 3)$; the point P_2 is $(-4, 3)$; etc. Locating a point when its coördinates are given is called **plotting** the point. It is convenient to plot a point, say P_1, by laying off $OM = x$ and then $MP_1 = y$.

The coördinate axes divide the plane into four parts called **quadrants**, numbered as indicated in Fig. 1 — I, II, III, IV.

3. Directed line segments. A **line segment** is that part of a line which is terminated by two given points on it. A **directed line segment** is a line segment to which either a positive or a negative direction has been assigned. If a positive direction is assigned to the line segment drawn from A to B (read AB), the opposite direction, from B to A, is negative, and vice versa. In either case

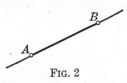

FIG. 2

$$BA = -AB \quad \text{or} \quad AB = -BA.$$

In Fig. 1, for example, NP_1 and MP_1 are line segments. It should be noticed that the abscissa of P_1 is the measure of the line segment directed from N to P_1, not from P_1 to N; while the ordinate of P_1 is the measure of the line segment directed from M to P_1, not from P_1 to M. Is the abscissa of P_2 the measure of NP_2 or P_2N?

4. Length of a line segment paralle Let P_1P_2 be a line segment parallel to t three cases as shown in the accompan and M_2 be points on the *x*-axis whose a as those of P_1 and P_2, respectively. figures $\qquad P_1P_2 = M_1M_2.$

In Fig. 3, *a*, $M_1M_2 = OM_2 - OM_1 =$
In Fig. 3, *b*, $M_1M_2 = M_1O + OM_2 = O$
In Fig. 3, *c*, $M_1M_2 = M_1O - M_2O = O$

Thus in each of the three cases we can of P_1P_2 is equal to the abscissa x_2 of the the abscissa x_1 of the beginning point P_1.

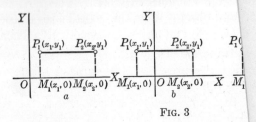

FIG. 3

In a similar manner it can be shown that t segment Q_1Q_2 parallel to the *y*-axis is equal the end point Q_2 minus the ordinate of the be

What is the change in temperature if t mercury column in a thermometer chang mark to the 20° mark? from $-12°$ to 20° $-8°$? from 8° to $-20°$?

5. Areas of triangles and polygons. If one si is parallel to an axis, that side may be cons and the altitude drawn to it is parallel to lengths may be calculated and the area compu the base times the altitude. If the vertices that no side is parallel to an axis, auxiliary drawn in such a way that the required area puted by combining the areas of trapezoids

4. Plot on one diagram the points (a, b), $(- a, b)$, $(- a, - b)$, and $(a, - b)$. Describe the position of the latter three points with respect to the position of the first point.

5. In what quadrants do those points lie whose abscissas and ordinates have like signs? unlike signs?

6. Describe the position of all points (a) whose abscissas have the same value; (b) whose ordinates have the same value.

7. Describe the position of all points (a) whose abscissas are zero; (b) whose ordinates are zero.

8. Describe the position of all points whose abscissas and ordinates are equal.

9. Find the length of the line segment directed from

(a) $(- 4, 0)$ to $(6, 0)$.   (c) $(2, - 7)$ to $(2, 8)$.
(b) $(8, 3)$ to $(- 4, 3)$.   (d) $(- 1, - 1)$ to $(- 1, - 7)$.

10. Find the area of the triangle whose vertices are

(a) $(2, 1)$, $(8, 3)$, and $(4, 7)$.
(b) $(- 5, - 4)$, $(7, - 2)$, and $(- 1, 6)$.
(c) $(- 4, 0)$, $(3, 0)$, and $(5, 10)$.
(d) $(- 3, - 4)$, $(5, - 2)$, and $(8, 6)$.
(e) $(0, 0)$, (a, b), and (b, a).

11. Find the area of the quadrilateral whose vertices are $(6, 10)$, $(- 1, 6)$, $(- 4, - 2)$, and $(8, - 3)$.

12. Find the area of the polygon whose vertices are $(5, 2)$, $(3, 10)$, $(- 4, 6)$, $(- 3, 0)$, and $(1, - 2)$.

6. Distance between any two points. Let $P_1(x_1, y_1)$ and $P_2(x_2, y_2)$ be any two points in the plane (Fig. 5). Join P_1 and P_2 by a straight line. Through P_1 draw a line parallel to the x-axis and through P_2 draw a line parallel to the y-axis. These lines intersect in $M(x_2, y_1)$. The triangle $P_1 M P_2$ is a right triangle. Hence

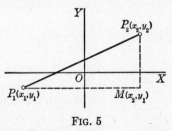

FIG. 5

$$\overline{P_1 P_2}^2 = \overline{P_1 M}^2 + \overline{M P_2}^2 = (x_2 - x_1)^2 + (y_2 - y_1)^2,$$

and
$$P_1 P_2 = \sqrt{(x_2 - x_1)^2 + (y_2 - y_1)^2}. \tag{1}$$

EXAMPLE 1. Find the distance between $(-3, -6)$ and $(5, -2)$.

Choosing $(-3, -6)$ for (x_2, y_2) and using equation (1), we have distance

$$d = \sqrt{[-3-5]^2 + [-6-(-2)]^2} = \sqrt{64+16} = \sqrt{80} = 4\sqrt{5}.$$

The positive sign is used before the radical since we are seeking the numerical measure of the distance between the points without regard to the direction in which it is measured. It is also to be noted that $(x_2 - x_1)^2 = (x_1 - x_2)^2$ and $(y_2 - y_1)^2 = (y_1 - y_2)^2$, and hence either point might have been chosen for (x_2, y_2).

If the line segment joining the given points is parallel to an axis, it is recommended that the distance be found directly as explained in Sec. 4, on page 5.

EXAMPLE 2. In the right triangle ACB, one leg is the line segment joining $A(-2, 3)$ and $C(6, -3)$. Find the coördinates of the third vertex B if the leg CB is 5 units in length.

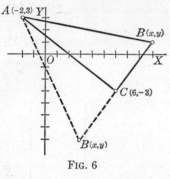

FIG. 6

Locate the points A and C on a set of axes. We see that the third vertex may be in either position marked $B(x, y)$ (located approximately). Our problem is to find the values of x and y. Since there are two unknowns, x and y, we shall need two equations. For either point B we have, by the conditions of our problem,

$$CB = 5 \quad \text{and} \quad \overline{AB}^2 = \overline{AC}^2 + 5^2.$$

But
$$CB = \sqrt{(x-6)^2 + (y+3)^2},$$
$$\overline{AB}^2 = (x+2)^2 + (y-3)^2,$$
$$\overline{AC}^2 = (-2-6)^2 + (3+3)^2 = 100.$$

Hence we must solve simultaneously the two equations

$$\sqrt{(x-6)^2 + (y+3)^2} = 5 \text{ and } (x+2)^2 + (y-3)^2 = 100 + 25,$$

which become, on simplifying,

$$x^2 + y^2 - 12\,x + 6\,y + 20 = 0$$

and

$$x^2 + y^2 + 4\,x - 6\,y - 112 = 0.$$

The simultaneous solutions of these two equations are $x = 9, y = 1$ and $x = 3, y = -7$. Hence there are two points, $B(9, 1)$ and $B(3, -7)$, each of which may serve as the third vertex of the required triangle.

EXERCISES

1. Find the distance between

(a) $(-3, 1)$ and $(5, 7)$.

(b) $(2, 6)$ and $(7, -6)$.

(c) $(0, 4)$ and $(6, 0)$.

(d) $(-4, -2)$ and $(5, 1)$.

(e) $(0, 0)$ and $(6, 3)$.

(f) $(2, 1)$ and $(3, -6)$.

2. Find the perimeter of the triangle whose vertices are $(-4, 3)$, $(5, 3)$, and $(11, -5)$.

3. Show that the triangle whose vertices are $(-3, 0)$, $(1, -2)$, and $(5, 6)$ is a right triangle.

4. Show that the triangle whose vertices are $(-1, 3)$, $(7, -5)$, and $(8, 4)$ is isosceles.

5. Show that a circle whose center is $(5, 5)$ can be drawn through $(6, -7)$, $(-3, -4)$, and $(-7, 6)$.

6. Find the length of each diagonal of the quadrilateral whose vertices are $(6, 2)$, $(0, 7)$, $(-5, 0)$, and $(2, -4)$.

7. Establish the generality of formula (1) (that is, show that it is true no matter in which quadrants the points P_1 and P_2 lie) by applying the argument of Sec. 4.

8. Find the point on the x-axis equidistant from $(2, 9)$ and $(10, 3)$.

9. Find the point on the y-axis equidistant from $(2, 9)$ and $(10, 3)$.

10. Find the point equidistant from $(-1, 9)$, $(5, 3)$, and $(3, -3)$.

11. Find the center of the circle which passes through $(3, 11)$, $(-10, -2)$, and $(6, -10)$.

12. Find the point whose ordinate equals its abscissa and which is equidistant from $(-2, 1)$ and $(6, -3)$.

13. Two vertices of an equilateral triangle are $(0, 0)$ and $(8, 6)$. Find a third vertex.

14. A right triangle having its legs 8 units and 6 units, respectively, is inscribed in a circle with center at the origin. Find the coördinates of the vertex of the right angle if the hypotenuse lies on the x-axis.

7. Point of division. The coördinates of a point P on the line segment P_1P_2 (Fig. 7) such that $P_1P/PP_2 = r_1/r_2$ can be found by the following method. Through P_1, P, and P_2, respectively, draw P_1M_1, PM, and P_2M_2 perpendicular to the x-axis. We have

FIG. 7

$$\frac{P_1P}{PP_2} = \frac{M_1M}{MM_2} = \frac{x - x_1}{x_2 - x}.$$

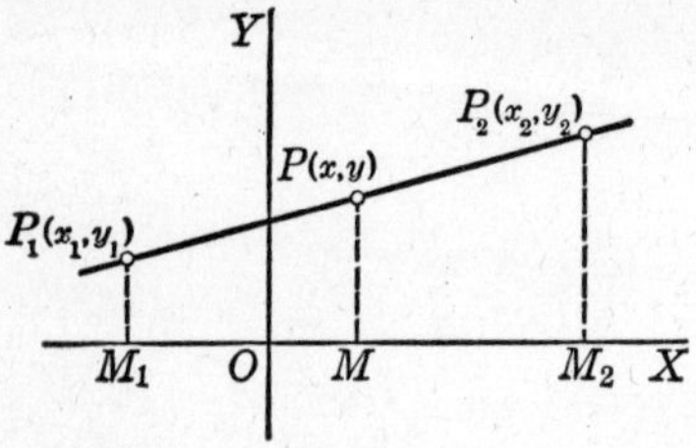

But $P_1P/PP_2 = r_1/r_2$. Hence

$$\frac{x - x_1}{x_2 - x} = \frac{r_1}{r_2}.$$

Solving for x, we have

$$x = \frac{r_1x_2 + r_2x_1}{r_1 + r_2}. \qquad (2)$$

Similarly, by drawing lines through P_1, P, and P_2 perpendicular to the y-axis, we can show that

$$y = \frac{r_1y_2 + r_2y_1}{r_1 + r_2}. \qquad (3)$$

In case the ratio r_1/r_2 is negative, the line segments P_1P and PP_2 must be opposite in sign, that is, must be measured in opposite directions. In this case P is not between P_1 and P_2. If the ratio r_1/r_2 is numerically greater than 1, the segment P_1P is numerically greater than PP_2 and P lies beyond P_2 on P_1P_2 produced. If the ratio is numerically less than 1, then P lies beyond P_1 on P_2P_1 produced. In either case it can be shown that the coördinates (x, y) of the point of division are given by the equations (2) and (3).

An important particular case of finding the point of division occurs if P is the midpoint of P_1P_2. In this case $r_1 = r_2$ and the above equations (2) and (3) become

$$x = \frac{x_1 + x_2}{2}, \quad y = \frac{y_1 + y_2}{2}. \qquad (4)$$

EXAMPLE. Find the points which divide the line segment joining $(-3, 5)$ and $(7, -2)$ into three equal parts.

Call P_1 the point $(-3, 5)$ and P_2 the point $(7, -2)$. Then for the point of division nearest P_1 we shall have P_1P equal to one third and PP_2 equal to two thirds of the segment. Hence $r_1/r_2 = \frac{1}{2}$. Using equations (2) and (3),

$$x = \frac{1 \cdot 7 + 2 \cdot (-3)}{1 + 2} = \frac{1}{3}, \quad y = \frac{1 \cdot (-2) + 2 \cdot 5}{1 + 2} = 2\tfrac{2}{3}.$$

For the other point of division $r_1/r_2 = 2/1$. Hence

$$x = \frac{2 \cdot 7 + 1 \cdot (-3)}{1 + 2} = 3\tfrac{2}{3}, \quad y = \frac{2 \cdot (-2) + 1 \cdot 5}{1 + 2} = \frac{1}{3}.$$

Therefore the points of trisection of the given line segment are $(\tfrac{1}{3}, 2\tfrac{2}{3})$ and $(3\tfrac{2}{3}, \tfrac{1}{3})$.

EXERCISES

1. Derive formulas (4) directly from a figure.

2. Find the midpoints of the sides of a triangle whose vertices are $(5, 8)$, $(-3, 0)$, and $(3, -4)$.

3. Find the three points which divide into four equal parts the line segment joining $(-6, -3)$ and $(10, 4)$.

4. Show that the line segment joining $A(-3, 2)$ and $B(5, 4)$ and the line segment joining $C(-6, 9)$ and $D(8, -3)$ bisect each other.

5. Find the area of the triangle in Exercise 4, page 9, by using the formula $A = \tfrac{1}{2} bh$.

6. The line segment AB has for its end points $A(-4, 1)$ and $B(11, 6)$. Find the point C such that (a) $AC/CB = \tfrac{2}{3}$; (b) $AC/CB = -\tfrac{2}{3}$; (c) $AC/CB = -\tfrac{3}{2}$.

7. Find the two points on the line through $(-5, -2)$ and $(7, 4)$ each of which is five times as far from the first point as from the second.

worked

8. The line segment drawn from $(-5, 1)$ to $(1, 3)$ is extended 10 units. Find the coördinates of the end point.

9. A line is drawn across the triangle $A(-4, -3)$, $B(8, 0)$, and $C(6, 12)$ parallel to the base AB, and crossing the side AC at $(0, 3)$. Find the point where it crosses BC.

10. Find the length of each median of the triangle whose vertices are $(5, 6)$, $(-5, 2)$, and $(9, -2)$.

11. Find the point on each median in Exercise 10 which is at a distance from the vertex equal to two thirds of the length of the median.

12. The vertices of a triangle are (x_1, y_1), (x_2, y_2), and (x_3, y_3). Show that the point on each median which is at a distance from the vertex equal to two thirds of the length of the median is $\left(\dfrac{x_1 + x_2 + x_3}{3}, \dfrac{y_1 + y_2 + y_3}{3}\right)$. (This point is called the centroid of the triangle.)

13. The midpoints of the sides of a triangle are $(5, 3)$, $(1, 5)$, and $(-1, -1)$. Find the vertices.

worked

14. The ends of a chord of a circle whose radius is $5\sqrt{2}$ are $(3, -4)$ and $(5, 2)$. Find the center of the circle.

15. The base of an isosceles triangle joins the points $(0, 0)$ and $(8, -6)$. The altitude is 5 units. Find the coördinates of the vertex.

8. Slope of a line. It is convenient to give the direction of a line by means of the tangent of the angle θ (Fig. 8, a and b), $0 \leqq \theta < 180°$, measured from the positive direction of the

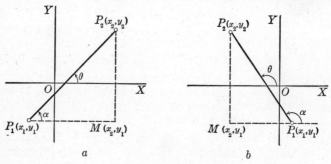

a b

Fig. 8

PLANE ANALYTIC GEOMETRY

CHAPTER I

THE POINT

1. Definition. Analytic geometry is a branch of mathematics in which one studies geometry by means of algebra. A correspondence is set up between a geometric locus and one or more equations, and properties of the locus are determined from the equations. In order to connect algebra and geometry use is made of a coördinate system which furnishes a means for locating points in a plane or in space.

2. Rectangular coördinates. In the coördinate system employed most frequently two straight lines intersecting at right angles* are used as lines of reference. A point is located in the plane of these lines by giving its perpendicular distance and direction from each of them. The distances with signs indicating directions are called the coördinates of the point. The lines from which distances are measured are called the axes of coördinates, or briefly

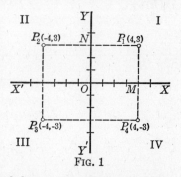

Fig. 1

axes. The point of intersection of the axes is called the **origin** of coördinates, or the origin. In Fig. 1 the line XOX' is

---

* Two lines not at right angles may be used, but the resulting algebra is, in general, more complicated than in the case of lines at right angles. Any system of coördinates using two intersecting lines as axes is called Cartesian after Réne Descartes (1596–1650), a French mathematician.

called the x-axis, and the line YOY' is called the y-axis. Distances measured to the right of the y-axis are usually called positive and those measured to the left negative. Distances measured upward from the x-axis are usually called positive and those measured downward negative. The choice of positive direction is a matter of convenience and may change from problem to problem.

That coördinate which indicates the distance of a point to the right or to the left of the y-axis is called the **abscissa**, or **x-coördinate** of the point; and that coördinate which indicates the distance above or below the x-axis is called the **ordinate**, or the **y-coördinate** of the point. The position of a point is indicated by writing its coördinates in a parenthesis, thus: (abscissa, ordinate). For example, the point P_1 in Fig. 1 is (NP_1, MP_1), or (4, 3); the point P_2 is $(-4, 3)$; etc. Locating a point when its coördinates are given is called **plotting** the point. It is convenient to plot a point, say P_1, by laying off $OM = x$ and then $MP_1 = y$.

The coördinate axes divide the plane into four parts called **quadrants**, numbered as indicated in Fig. 1 — I, II, III, IV.

3. Directed line segments. A **line segment** is that part of a line which is terminated by two given points on it. A **directed line segment** is a line segment to which either a positive or a negative direction has been assigned. If a positive direction is assigned to the line segment drawn from A to B (read AB), the opposite direction, from B to A, is negative, and vice versa. In either case

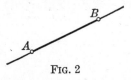

FIG. 2

$$BA = -AB \quad \text{or} \quad AB = -BA.$$

In Fig. 1, for example, NP_1 and MP_1 are line segments. It should be noticed that the abscissa of P_1 is the measure of the line segment directed from N to P_1, not from P_1 to N; while the ordinate of P_1 is the measure of the line segment directed from M to P_1, not from P_1 to M. Is the abscissa of P_2 the measure of NP_2 or P_2N?

4. Length of a line segment parallel to a coördinate axis.
Let P_1P_2 be a line segment parallel to the x-axis and consider
three cases as shown in the accompanying figures. Let M_1
and M_2 be points on the x-axis whose abscissas are the same
as those of P_1 and P_2, respectively. In each of the three
figures
$$P_1P_2 = M_1M_2.$$

In Fig. 3, a, $M_1M_2 = OM_2 - OM_1 = x_2 - x_1$.
In Fig. 3, b, $M_1M_2 = M_1O + OM_2 = OM_2 - OM_1 = x_2 - x_1$.
In Fig. 3, c, $M_1M_2 = M_1O - M_2O = OM_2 - OM_1 = x_2 - x_1$.

Thus in each of the three cases we can say that the length
of P_1P_2 is equal to the abscissa x_2 of the end point P_2 minus
the abscissa x_1 of the beginning point P_1.

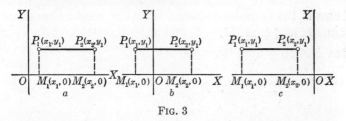

Fig. 3

In a similar manner it can be shown that the length of a line
segment Q_1Q_2 parallel to the y-axis is equal to the ordinate of
the end point Q_2 minus the ordinate of the beginning point Q_1.

What is the change in temperature if the height of the
mercury column in a thermometer changes from the 12°
mark to the 20° mark? from $-12°$ to 20°? from $-12°$ to
$-8°$? from 8° to $-20°$?

5. Areas of triangles and polygons. If one side of a triangle
is parallel to an axis, that side may be considered the base
and the altitude drawn to it is parallel to an axis. Their
lengths may be calculated and the area computed as one half
the base times the altitude. If the vertices are so located
that no side is parallel to an axis, auxiliary lines may be
drawn in such a way that the required area may be computed by combining the areas of trapezoids and triangles

with sides and altitudes parallel to the axes. Or the triangle may be inclosed in a rectangle with sides parallel to the axes and the required area found by subtracting the areas of right triangles from the area of the rectangle. The following example illustrates the use of a trapezoid and triangles.

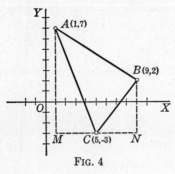

FIG. 4

EXAMPLE. Find the area of the triangle whose vertices are $A(1, 7)$, $B(9, 2)$, and $C(5, -3)$.

Draw through the vertices of the triangle the auxiliary lines MN, AM, and BN, as shown in the figure and observe that the coördinates of the points M and N are $(1, -3)$ and $(9, -3)$, respectively. Then

area $\triangle ABC =$ area trapezoid $AMNB$

$$- \text{area} \triangle AMC - \text{area} \triangle BNC$$

$$= \frac{MA + NB}{2} \cdot MN - \frac{MA \cdot MC}{2} - \frac{CN \cdot NB}{2}$$

$$= \frac{10 + 5}{2} \cdot 8 - \frac{10 \cdot 4}{2} - \frac{4 \cdot 5}{2} = 30.$$

The area of any polygon may be found in a similar manner.

EXERCISES

1. Plot the following points:

$P_1(2, 3)$; $P_3(-3, 5)$; $P_5(7, 0)$; $P_7(-5, 0)$;
$P_2(4, -1)$; $P_4(-6, -2)$; $P_6(0, -4)$; $P_8(0, 0)$.

2. Plot the following points on the same diagram: $(-4, 3)$; $(-2, 2\frac{1}{2})$; $(0, 2)$; $(2, \frac{3}{2})$; $(4, 1)$; $(8, 0)$; $(10, -\frac{1}{2})$; and $(12, -1)$. What apparent characteristic does this set of points possess?

3. Plot the following points and connect them by a smooth curve in the order of increasing abscissas: $(-4, -6.6)$; $(-3, 0)$; $(-2, 3)$; $(-1, 3.6)$; $(0, 3)$; $(1, 2.4)$; $(2, 3)$; $(2.5, 3.9)$; and $(3, 6)$. Would the shape of the curve be materially changed if the points $(-1, 3.6)$ and $(1, 2.4)$ were omitted?

4. Plot on one diagram the points (a, b), $(-a, b)$, $(-a, -b)$, and $(a, -b)$. Describe the position of the latter three points with respect to the position of the first point.

5. In what quadrants do those points lie whose abscissas and ordinates have like signs? unlike signs?

6. Describe the position of all points (a) whose abscissas have the same value; (b) whose ordinates have the same value.

7. Describe the position of all points (a) whose abscissas are zero; (b) whose ordinates are zero.

8. Describe the position of all points whose abscissas and ordinates are equal.

9. Find the length of the line segment directed from

    (a) $(-4, 0)$ to $(6, 0)$. (c) $(2, -7)$ to $(2, 8)$.

    (b) $(8, 3)$ to $(-4, 3)$. (d) $(-1, -1)$ to $(-1, -7)$.

10. Find the area of the triangle whose vertices are

    (a) $(2, 1)$, $(8, 3)$, and $(4, 7)$.

    (b) $(-5, -4)$, $(7, -2)$, and $(-1, 6)$.

    (c) $(-4, 0)$, $(3, 0)$, and $(5, 10)$.

    (d) $(-3, -4)$, $(5, -2)$, and $(8, 6)$.

    (e) $(0, 0)$, (a, b), and (b, a).

11. Find the area of the quadrilateral whose vertices are $(6, 10)$, $(-1, 6)$, $(-4, -2)$, and $(8, -3)$.

12. Find the area of the polygon whose vertices are $(5, 2)$, $(3, 10)$, $(-4, 6)$, $(-3, 0)$, and $(1, -2)$.

6. Distance between any two points. Let $P_1(x_1, y_1)$ and $P_2(x_2, y_2)$ be any two points in the plane (Fig. 5). Join P_1 and P_2 by a straight line. Through P_1 draw a line parallel to the x-axis and through P_2 draw a line parallel to the y-axis. These lines intersect in $M(x_2, y_1)$. The triangle P_1MP_2 is a right triangle. Hence

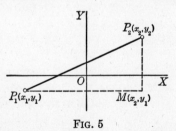

FIG. 5

$$\overline{P_1P_2}^2 = \overline{P_1M}^2 + \overline{MP_2}^2 = (x_2 - x_1)^2 + (y_2 - y_1)^2,$$

and $$P_1P_2 = \sqrt{(x_2 - x_1)^2 + (y_2 - y_1)^2}. \qquad (1)$$

EXAMPLE 1. Find the distance between $(-3, -6)$ and $(5, -2)$.

Choosing $(-3, -6)$ for (x_2, y_2) and using equation (1), we have distance

$$d = \sqrt{[-3 - 5]^2 + [-6 - (-2)]^2} = \sqrt{64 + 16} = \sqrt{80} = 4\sqrt{5}.$$

The positive sign is used before the radical since we are seeking the numerical measure of the distance between the points without regard to the direction in which it is measured. It is also to be noted that $(x_2 - x_1)^2 = (x_1 - x_2)^2$ and $(y_2 - y_1)^2 = (y_1 - y_2)^2$, and hence either point might have been chosen for (x_2, y_2).

If the line segment joining the given points is parallel to an axis, it is recommended that the distance be found directly as explained in Sec. 4, on page 5.

EXAMPLE 2. In the right triangle ACB, one leg is the line segment joining $A(-2, 3)$ and $C(6, -3)$. Find the coördinates of the third vertex B if the leg CB is 5 units in length.

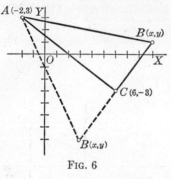

FIG. 6

Locate the points A and C on a set of axes. We see that the third vertex may be in either position marked $B(x, y)$ (located approximately). Our problem is to find the values of x and y. Since there are two unknowns, x and y, we shall need two equations. For either point B we have, by the conditions of our problem,

$$CB = 5 \quad \text{and} \quad \overline{AB}^2 = \overline{AC}^2 + 5^2.$$

But
$$CB = \sqrt{(x - 6)^2 + (y + 3)^2},$$
$$\overline{AB}^2 = (x + 2)^2 + (y - 3)^2,$$
$$\overline{AC}^2 = (-2 - 6)^2 + (3 + 3)^2 = 100.$$

Hence we must solve simultaneously the two equations

$$\sqrt{(x-6)^2 + (y+3)^2} = 5 \text{ and } (x+2)^2 + (y-3)^2 = 100 + 25,$$

which become, on simplifying,

$$x^2 + y^2 - 12\,x + 6\,y + 20 = 0$$

and $$x^2 + y^2 + 4\,x - 6\,y - 112 = 0.$$

The simultaneous solutions of these two equations are $x = 9, y = 1$ and $x = 3, y = -7$. Hence there are two points, $B(9, 1)$ and $B(3, -7)$, each of which may serve as the third vertex of the required triangle.

EXERCISES

1. Find the distance between

(a) $(-3, 1)$ and $(5, 7)$.

(b) $(2, 6)$ and $(7, -6)$.

(c) $(0, 4)$ and $(6, 0)$.

(d) $(-4, -2)$ and $(5, 1)$.

(e) $(0, 0)$ and $(6, 3)$.

(f) $(2, 1)$ and $(3, -6)$.

2. Find the perimeter of the triangle whose vertices are $(-4, 3)$, $(5, 3)$, and $(11, -5)$.

3. Show that the triangle whose vertices are $(-3, 0)$, $(1, -2)$, and $(5, 6)$ is a right triangle.

4. Show that the triangle whose vertices are $(-1, 3)$, $(7, -5)$, and $(8, 4)$ is isosceles.

5. Show that a circle whose center is $(5, 5)$ can be drawn through $(6, -7)$, $(-3, -4)$, and $(-7, 6)$.

6. Find the length of each diagonal of the quadrilateral whose vertices are $(6, 2)$, $(0, 7)$, $(-5, 0)$, and $(2, -4)$.

7. Establish the generality of formula (1) (that is, show that it is true no matter in which quadrants the points P_1 and P_2 lie) by applying the argument of Sec. 4.

8. Find the point on the x-axis equidistant from $(2, 9)$ and $(10, 3)$.

9. Find the point on the y-axis equidistant from $(2, 9)$ and $(10, 3)$.

10. Find the point equidistant from $(-1, 9)$, $(5, 3)$, and $(3, -3)$.

11. Find the center of the circle which passes through $(3, 11)$, $(-10, -2)$, and $(6, -10)$.

12. Find the point whose ordinate equals its abscissa and which is equidistant from $(-2, 1)$ and $(6, -3)$.

13. Two vertices of an equilateral triangle are $(0, 0)$ and $(8, 6)$. Find a third vertex.

14. A right triangle having its legs 8 units and 6 units, respectively, is inscribed in a circle with center at the origin. Find the coördinates of the vertex of the right angle if the hypotenuse lies on the x-axis.

7. Point of division. The coördinates of a point P on the line segment P_1P_2 (Fig. 7) such that $P_1P/PP_2 = r_1/r_2$ can be found by the following method. Through P_1, P, and P_2, respectively, draw P_1M_1, PM, and P_2M_2 perpendicular to the x-axis. We have

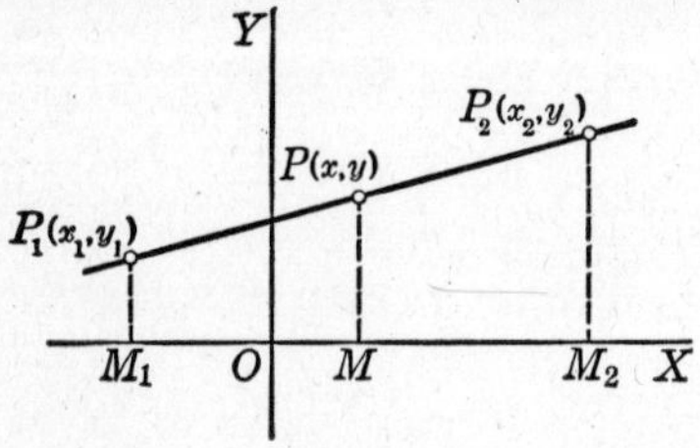

FIG. 7

$$\frac{P_1P}{PP_2} = \frac{M_1M}{MM_2} = \frac{x - x_1}{x_2 - x}.$$

But $P_1P/PP_2 = r_1/r_2$. Hence

$$\frac{x - x_1}{x_2 - x} = \frac{r_1}{r_2}.$$

Solving for x, we have

$$x = \frac{r_1x_2 + r_2x_1}{r_1 + r_2}. \qquad (2)$$

Similarly, by drawing lines through P_1, P, and P_2 perpendicular to the y-axis, we can show that

$$y = \frac{r_1y_2 + r_2y_1}{r_1 + r_2}. \qquad (3)$$

In case the ratio r_1/r_2 is negative, the line segments P_1P and PP_2 must be opposite in sign, that is, must be measured in opposite directions. In this case P is not between P_1 and P_2. If the ratio r_1/r_2 is numerically greater than 1, the segment P_1P is numerically greater than PP_2 and P lies beyond P_2 on P_1P_2 produced. If the ratio is numerically less than 1, then P lies beyond P_1 on P_2P_1 produced. In either case it can be shown that the coördinates (x, y) of the point of division are given by the equations (2) and (3).

An important particular case of finding the point of division occurs if P is the midpoint of P_1P_2. In this case $r_1 = r_2$ and the above equations (2) and (3) become

$$x = \frac{x_1 + x_2}{2}, \quad y = \frac{y_1 + y_2}{2}. \tag{4}$$

EXAMPLE. Find the points which divide the line segment joining $(-3, 5)$ and $(7, -2)$ into three equal parts.

Call P_1 the point $(-3, 5)$ and P_2 the point $(7, -2)$. Then for the point of division nearest P_1 we shall have P_1P equal to one third and PP_2 equal to two thirds of the segment. Hence $r_1/r_2 = \frac{1}{2}$. Using equations (2) and (3),

$$x = \frac{1 \cdot 7 + 2 \cdot (-3)}{1 + 2} = \frac{1}{3}, \quad y = \frac{1 \cdot (-2) + 2 \cdot 5}{1 + 2} = 2\frac{2}{3}.$$

For the other point of division $r_1/r_2 = 2/1$. Hence

$$x = \frac{2 \cdot 7 + 1 \cdot (-3)}{1 + 2} = 3\frac{2}{3}, \quad y = \frac{2 \cdot (-2) + 1 \cdot 5}{1 + 2} = \frac{1}{3}.$$

Therefore the points of trisection of the given line segment are $(\frac{1}{3}, 2\frac{2}{3})$ and $(3\frac{2}{3}, \frac{1}{3})$.

EXERCISES

1. Derive formulas (4) directly from a figure.

2. Find the midpoints of the sides of a triangle whose vertices are $(5, 8)$, $(-3, 0)$, and $(3, -4)$.

3. Find the three points which divide into four equal parts the line segment joining $(-6, -3)$ and $(10, 4)$.

4. Show that the line segment joining $A(-3, 2)$ and $B(5, 4)$ and the line segment joining $C(-6, 9)$ and $D(8, -3)$ bisect each other.

5. Find the area of the triangle in Exercise 4, page 9, by using the formula $A = \frac{1}{2} bh$.

6. The line segment AB has for its end points $A(-4, 1)$ and $B(11, 6)$. Find the point C such that (a) $AC/CB = \frac{2}{3}$; (b) $AC/CB = -\frac{2}{3}$; (c) $AC/CB = -\frac{3}{2}$.

7. Find the two points on the line through $(-5, -2)$ and $(7, 4)$ each of which is five times as far from the first point as from the second.

8. The line segment drawn from $(-5, 1)$ to $(1, 3)$ is extended 10 units. Find the coördinates of the end point.

9. A line is drawn across the triangle $A(-4, -3)$, $B(8, 0)$, and $C(6, 12)$ parallel to the base AB, and crossing the side AC at $(0, 3)$. Find the point where it crosses BC.

10. Find the length of each median of the triangle whose vertices are $(5, 6)$, $(-5, 2)$, and $(9, -2)$.

11. Find the point on each median in Exercise 10 which is at a distance from the vertex equal to two thirds of the length of the median.

12. The vertices of a triangle are (x_1, y_1), (x_2, y_2), and (x_3, y_3). Show that the point on each median which is at a distance from the vertex equal to two thirds of the length of the median is $\left(\dfrac{x_1 + x_2 + x_3}{3}, \dfrac{y_1 + y_2 + y_3}{3}\right)$. (This point is called the centroid of the triangle.)

13. The midpoints of the sides of a triangle are $(5, 3)$, $(1, 5)$, and $(-1, -1)$. Find the vertices.

14. The ends of a chord of a circle whose radius is $5\sqrt{2}$ are $(3, -4)$ and $(5, 2)$. Find the center of the circle.

15. The base of an isosceles triangle joins the points $(0, 0)$ and $(8, -6)$. The altitude is 5 units. Find the coördinates of the vertex.

8. Slope of a line. It is convenient to give the direction of a line by means of the tangent of the angle θ (Fig. 8, a and b), $0 \leqq \theta < 180°$, measured from the positive direction of the

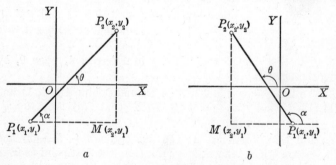

a b

Fig. 8

x-axis to the line. The angle θ is called the **angle of inclination,** and its tangent, usually denoted by m, is called the **slope** of the line.

The slope of the line segment P_1P_2 in Fig. 8 (*a* and *b*) is easily expressed in terms of the coördinates of P_1 and P_2 by drawing the triangle P_1MP_2. In either figure the slope m of the line is given by

$$m = \tan \theta = \tan \alpha = \frac{MP_2}{P_1M},$$

or $$m = \frac{y_2 - y_1}{x_2 - x_1}. \tag{5}$$

Since $$\frac{y_2 - y_1}{x_2 - x_1} = \frac{y_1 - y_2}{x_1 - x_2},$$

it is evident that the slope of a line may be interpreted as the ratio of the change in vertical distance to the change in horizontal distance as a point moves along the line in either direction.

EXAMPLE. Find the slope of the line through $(2, 3)$ and $(5, -4)$.

Using equation (5), we have

$$m = \frac{-4 - 3}{5 - 2} = -\frac{7}{3}.$$

9. Parallel lines. Perpendicular lines. Two lines which are parallel have equal angles of inclination and therefore have equal slopes, and conversely.

If two lines, having slopes $m_1 = \tan \theta_1$ and $m_2 = \tan \theta_2$, meet at right angles, as in Fig. 9, then $\theta_2 = 90° + \theta_1$ and

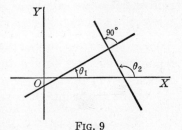

FIG. 9

$$m_2 = \tan \theta_2 = \tan (90° + \theta_1) = -\cot \theta_1 = -\frac{1}{\tan \theta_1},$$

or $$m_2 = -\frac{1}{m_1}.$$

Hence two lines which are perpendicular have slopes which are negative reciprocals each of the other, and conversely.

EXAMPLE. Find the slope of a line perpendicular to the line segment joining the points $(2, 3)$ and $(5, -4)$.

The slope of the line segment joining the given points was found in the example at the end of the last section to be $-\frac{7}{3}$. The negative reciprocal of this number is $\frac{3}{7}$. Hence any line with slope $\frac{3}{7}$ will be perpendicular to the line through $(2, 3)$ and $(5, -4)$.

10. Angle of intersection of two lines. Let $m_1 = \tan \theta_1$ and $m_2 = \tan \theta_2$ be the slopes of the lines l_1 and l_2 (Fig. 10), re-

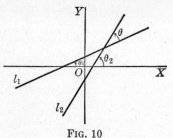

FIG. 10

spectively. Let θ be the angle measured from the line l_1 to the line l_2. Then $\theta = \theta_2 - \theta_1$ and

$$\tan \theta = \tan (\theta_2 - \theta_1)$$
$$= \frac{\tan \theta_2 - \tan \theta_1}{1 + \tan \theta_1 \tan \theta_2},$$

or $\tan \theta = \dfrac{m_2 - m_1}{1 + m_1 m_2}.$

It will be observed that the expression for tan θ gives the tangent of that angle θ which has the line with slope m_1 for its initial side and the line with slope m_2 for its terminal side, if θ is measured in the counter-clockwise direction.

EXAMPLE. Given a line through $A(1, 5)$ and $B(4, 1)$, and a line through $C(2, 6)$ and $D(3, -1)$, intersecting at E, find the tangent of the angle DEB.

Plotting the points, it is seen that DE is the initial side. Hence

$$m_1 = \frac{6 - (-1)}{2 - 3} = -7 \quad \text{and} \quad m_2 = \frac{5 - 1}{1 - 4} = -\frac{4}{3},$$

and $\tan \angle DEB = \dfrac{-\frac{4}{3} - (-7)}{1 + \frac{28}{3}} = \dfrac{17}{31}.$

We note that $\angle DEB$ is acute since its tangent is positive.

EXERCISES

1. Find the slope of the line segment joining

(a) $(2, 1)$ and $(5, 4)$.   (c) $(-2, 4)$ and $(7, -2)$.

(b) $(1, -3)$ and $(6, 7)$.   (d) $(-3, 2)$ and $(5, 2)$.

2. Draw the line through

(a) $(3, 0)$ with slope $\frac{1}{2}$.   (d) $(0, 0)$ with slope 4.

(b) $(3, 0)$ with slope $-\frac{1}{2}$. (e) $(0, 1)$ with slope $\frac{2}{3}$.

(c) $(0, 0)$ with slope $\frac{1}{4}$.   (f) $(0, 1)$ with slope $-\frac{3}{2}$.

3. Show that the line through $(3, 5)$ and $(7, -1)$ is

(a) parallel to the line through $(-4, 4)$ and $(0, -2)$;

(b) perpendicular to the line through $(0, 0)$ and $(12, 8)$.

4. Find the slopes of the medians of the triangle whose vertices are $(9, 2)$, $(3, 8)$, and $(-5, -4)$.

5. Show that

(a) $(5, 7)$, $(8, -5)$, and $(0, -7)$ are the vertices of a right triangle.

(b) $(4, 0)$, $(7, 8)$, $(0, 10)$, and $(-3, 2)$ are the vertices of a parallelogram.

(c) $(8, 0)$, $(6, 6)$, $(-3, 3)$, and $(-1, -3)$ are the vertices of a rectangle.

(d) $(10, 8)$, $(-3, 9)$, $(-4, -4)$, and $(9, -5)$ are the vertices of a square.

6. Show that the points $(-3, -7)$, $(0, -2)$, and $(6, 8)$ are collinear (that is, lie on the same straight line).

7. A line through $(7, 4)$ intersects a line through $(4, 9)$ at $(2, 1)$. Find the acute angle of intersection of the two lines.

8. Find the acute angle between the diagonals of the

(a) parallelogram in Exercise 5 (b);

(b) rectangle in Exercise 5 (c).

9. Find the angles of the triangle whose vertices are

(a) $(3, 7)$, $(-3, -2)$, and $(7, 0)$.

(b) $(8, 6)$, $(-4, 2)$, and $(1, -1)$.

(c) $(4, 6)$, $(-5, -3)$, and $(10, 0)$.

(d) $(0, 0)$, $(5, 0)$, and $(10, 5)$.

(e) $(0, 0)$, $(3\,a, 0)$, and $(a, 2\,a)$.

10. Show that $(-1, -3)$, $(8, 3)$, $(3, 4)$, and $(0, 2)$ are the vertices of an isosceles trapezoid.

11. The angle between two lines is $45°$. The slope of one of the lines is $\frac{3}{2}$. What is the slope of the other line?

12. The slope of the hypotenuse of an isosceles right triangle is -3. What are the slopes of the two legs?

13. Two vertices of an equilateral triangle are $(0, 0)$ and (a, a). Find the slopes of the three sides.

14. Find the angle between two lines whose slopes are m and $1/m$ respectively.

15. Show that if two lines have slopes m and $\dfrac{m-1}{m+1}$, respectively, they include an angle of $45°$.

11. Applications to elementary geometry. Choice of axes.
The methods of analytic geometry will be found more powerful in the attack upon many of the problems of geometry than the methods which the student has thus far employed. Analytic geometry not only simplifies the proofs of many of the propositions with which we are familiar, but enables us to attack successfully problems which we could handle in elementary geometry only with great difficulty, or not at all. That the tools already developed — the formulas for distance, point of division, and slope — will aid in solving problems of geometry is illustrated by the exercises at the end of this section.

The properties of a geometric figure depend upon the relations of the parts and not upon the particular position in which the figure is drawn. Hence the properties of any geometric figure are independent of the way in which the axes are chosen. In the proof of geometric properties of figures it will, in general, be possible to choose the axes in more than one way. The axes should be chosen in the way which gives the simplest algebra. If we have a vertex of the figure at the origin and some line of the figure for an axis we shall usually have the best choice of axes. Problems differ, however, and no general rule is without exception. Much must be left to the ingenuity of the student.

EXAMPLE. The line joining the midpoints of the nonparallel sides of a trapezoid is equal to one half of the sum of the parallel sides and is parallel to them.

Choose a base of the trapezoid for the x-axis and one end of that base for the origin, as in the figure. The coördinates of the four vertices may be taken as indicated.

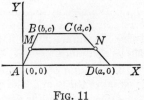

FIG. 11

The midpoint of AB is $(b/2, c/2)$ and of CD is $((a + d)/2, c/2)$. The slope of MN is found to be zero, and MN is therefore parallel to the x-axis and hence is parallel to AD and BC. Since MN is parallel to the x-axis, its length is

$$MN = \frac{a+d}{2} - \frac{b}{2} = \frac{a+d-b}{2}.$$

But $AD = a$ and $BC = d - b$. Hence

$$MN = \tfrac{1}{2}(AD + BC).$$

EXERCISES

Prove analytically:

1. The diagonals of a rectangle are equal.

2. The diagonals of a square are perpendicular to each other.

3. The diagonals of a parallelogram bisect each other.

4. The line segment drawn from the vertex of the right angle of a right triangle to the midpoint of the hypotenuse is equal to one half of the hypotenuse.

5. The line segment joining the midpoints of two sides of a triangle is equal to one half of the third side and is parallel to it.

6. If two medians of a triangle are equal the triangle is isosceles.

7. The diagonals of an isosceles trapezoid are equal.

8. The line segments which join the midpoints of the sides of a quadrilateral taken in order form a parallelogram.

9. The line segments which join the midpoints of the opposite sides of a quadrilateral bisect each other.

10. If O, A, B, and C are points on a straight line arranged in any order and P, Q, and R are the midpoints of the segments AB, BC, and AC, respectively, then $OP \cdot AB + OQ \cdot BC = OR \cdot AC$.

11. If a median is drawn from a vertex to the opposite side of a triangle, the sum of the squares of the other two sides is equal to twice the square of one half of the first side plus twice the square of the median.

12. The sum of the squares of the four sides of a quadrilateral is equal to the sum of the squares of the diagonals plus four times the square of the line segment which joins the midpoints of the diagonals.

13. In any triangle four times the sum of the squares of the medians is equal to three times the sum of the squares of the sides.

14. The area of a triangle whose vertices are (x_1, y_1), (x_2, y_2), and (x_3, y_3) is $\frac{1}{2}(x_1y_2 - x_2y_1 + x_2y_3 - x_3y_2 + x_3y_1 - x_1y_3)$.

15. Show that the area of the triangle in Exercise 14 can be expressed in the form

$$\text{Area} = \frac{1}{2}\begin{vmatrix} x_1 & y_1 & 1 \\ x_2 & y_2 & 1 \\ x_3 & y_3 & 1 \end{vmatrix}.$$

CHAPTER II

THE STRAIGHT LINE

12. Correspondence between geometric figure and equation.
The coördinate system described in Chapter I can be used
to set up a correspondence between equations and certain
geometric figures. In this chapter is discussed the correspondence between straight lines and first degree equations
in two variables. Two problems present themselves:

1. *Given the line to find the corresponding equation.*
2. *Given the equation to locate the corresponding line.*

The nature of these two problems will be illustrated by
examples.

EXAMPLE 1. Find the equation which expresses the relation between the abscissa and the ordinate of any (every)
point on the line through the point (3, 1) and with the slope $\frac{1}{2}$.

Let $P(x, y)$ be any point on the
given line. The slope of the line
segment joining P to (3, 1) is $\frac{1}{2}$.
The slope of this line segment
is also $(y - 1)/(x - 3)$. Hence

$$\frac{y-1}{x-3} = \frac{1}{2},$$

or $\qquad x - 2y = 1,$

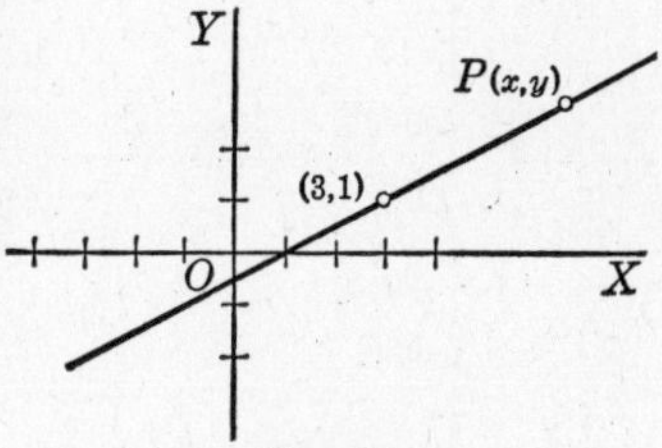

FIG. 12

is the equation expressing the relation between the abscissa
and the ordinate of any point on the line. It is called the
equation of the line. The equation is of the first degree. It
will be shown in Sec. 19 that to every straight line corresponds
an equation of the first degree in rectangular coördinates,
and conversely.

19

From the foregoing example we see that the coördinates x and y of every point (x, y) on the given line satisfy the equation corresponding to the line. This suggests the method of attack on problem 2, namely, that of locating a line when its equation is given. Pairs of numbers which satisfy an equation of the first degree in two variables are taken as abscissas and ordinates of points. These points when plotted lie on a straight line which corresponds to the given equation. This straight line is called the **graph** of the equation. *It is the line which passes through all the points, and only the points, whose coördinates satisfy the equation.*

EXAMPLE 2. Graph the line represented by the equation $2x - y = 6$.

The following pairs of numbers will be found to be solutions of the given equation:

$x =$	-2	-1	0	1	2	3	4	5	6
$y =$	-10	-8	-6	-4	-2	0	2	4	6

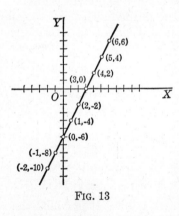

FIG. 13

Each pair of numbers represents a point on the required line. It is obviously impossible to write down all the number pairs which are solutions of the equation. If the points represented by these number pairs are plotted, they show the position of the line corresponding to the equation. Since the graph is a straight line, it is necessary to plot but two points, for example, the points $(0, -6)$ and $(3, 0)$.

The foregoing examples illustrate the correspondence between a straight line and its equation. The line is said to represent the equation *geometrically*; and the equation is said to represent the line algebraically or *analytically*.

13. Forms of equations of lines. The method of deriving the equation of a straight line depends upon the given geometric conditions which describe the line. A line is usually located by giving one point on it and its direction or slope, by giving two points on it, or by some other way which is essentially equivalent to one of these. Five typical forms of the equation of a straight line will be discussed. These forms are related and can be transformed from one into the other.

14. Equation of a line through a given point and with a given slope. Let $P_1(x_1, y_1)$ be the given point, and let m be the slope of a line through P_1. If $P(x, y)$ is any other point on the line, the slope of the line segment P_1P is m. The slope of the line segment P_1P is $(y - y_1)/(x - x_1)$. Hence the equation of the line through P_1 with slope m is

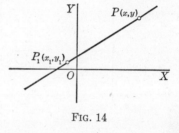

$$\frac{y - y_1}{x - x_1} = m,$$

FIG. 14

or $\quad y - y_1 = m(x - x_1).$ (1)

If the point (x_1, y_1) is the origin $(0, 0)$, the equation becomes

$$y = mx.$$

In case the line is parallel to the x-axis, the slope $m = 0$, and the equation becomes

$$y = y_1.$$

In case the line is parallel to the y-axis, the angle of inclination is 90°. But tan 90° is not a definite number and the slope form of the equation cannot be used. A line parallel to the y-axis is at a constant distance from it and hence, for such a line through P_1,

$$x = x_1.$$

For example, the equations of the two lines through $(-2, 6)$ parallel to the x- and y-axes, respectively, are $y = 6$ and $x = -2$.

EXAMPLE. Write the equation of the line through $(1, -2)$ perpendicular to the line through $(1, -2)$ and $(4, 3)$.

The slope of the segment joining $(1, -2)$ and $(4, 3)$ is $\frac{5}{3}$. The slope of the required line is therefore $-\frac{3}{5}$. Hence

$$y + 2 = -\tfrac{3}{5}(x - 1), \quad \text{or} \quad 3x + 5y + 7 = 0,$$

is the equation desired.

15. Equation of a line through two given points. Let $P_1(x_1, y_1)$ and $P_2(x_2, y_2)$ be two given points on a line whose equation is required, and let $P(x, y)$ be any other point on the line. The slope of the line segment PP_1 must be the same as the slope of the line segment P_1P_2. Hence the equation of the line is

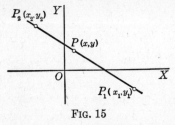

FIG. 15

$$\frac{y - y_1}{x - x_1} = \frac{y_2 - y_1}{x_2 - x_1},$$

or $y - y_1 = \dfrac{y_2 - y_1}{x_2 - x_1}(x - x_1).$ (2)

This is essentially the same as the case of a line through a point and with a given slope, since $(y_2 - y_1)/(x_2 - x_1)$ is the slope of the line joining (x_1, y_1) and (x_2, y_2). If $x_1 = x_2$ the line is parallel to the y-axis and the foregoing equation is not valid (see Sec. 14).

EXAMPLE. Write the equation of the line passing through $(-1, -4)$ and $(5, 5)$.

The slope is $\frac{3}{2}$. The equation of the line through the point $(-1, -4)$ and with slope $\frac{3}{2}$ is

$$y + 4 = \tfrac{3}{2}(x + 1), \quad \text{or} \quad 3x - 2y - 5 = 0.$$

16. Definition of intercepts. The **intercepts** of a line on the axes are the directed distances from the origin to the points where the line crosses the axes. To find the y-intercept let x equal zero in the equation of the line and solve for y; and to find the x-intercept let y equal zero and solve for x. For example, the x- and y-intercepts of the line $3x - 2y - 5 = 0$ are $\frac{5}{3}$ and $-\frac{5}{2}$, respectively.

EXERCISES

1. Find and plot at least five points which lie on the line whose equation is given. Draw the line in each case.

(a) $x + y = 5$.   (c) $5x + 3y + 2 = 0$.
(b) $3x - 2y = 6$.   (d) $x - 2y = 0$.

2. What are the x- and y-intercepts of each of the lines in Exercise 1?

3. Which of the following points lie on the line $3x - 5y + 1 = 0$?

(a) $(3, 2)$.   (c) $(1, 0.8)$.   (e) $(10, 6)$.   (g) $(8, 5)$.
(b) $(7, 4)$.   (d) $(-2, -1)$.   (f) $(-7, -4)$.   (h) $(0, 0)$.

4. How can one easily tell if a line whose equation is given goes through the origin? Which of the lines in Exercise 1 goes through the origin?

5. Write the equation of the line through $(3, -2)$

(a) with slope 2;   (d) parallel to the x-axis;
(b) and $(-1, 4)$;   (e) parallel to the y-axis;
(c) and the origin;   (f) with inclination angle $45°$.

6. Write the equations of the two lines through $(-1, 3)$ parallel and perpendicular, respectively, to the line through $(-3, -5)$ and $(9, 4)$.

7. Write the equation of the line which bisects

(a) the first and third quadrants;
(b) the second and fourth quadrants.

8. What line is represented by the equation (a) $x = 0$? (b) $y = 0$?

9. Write the equations of the four sides and the two diagonals of the rectangle whose vertices are $(0, 0)$, $(8, 0)$, $(8, 4)$, and $(0, 4)$.

10. Write the equations of the sides of the triangle whose vertices are $(5, 5)$, $(-5, 5)$, and $(0, 0)$.

11. Write the equations of the medians of the triangle whose vertices are $(6, 2)$, $(2, 6)$, and $(0, 0)$.

12. The midpoints of the sides of a triangle are $(3, 3)$, $(-1, 1)$, and $(0, -4)$. Write the equations of the sides of the triangle.

13. An isosceles right triangle lying in the first quadrant has the ends of its hypotenuse at $(0, 0)$ and $(0, 12)$. Write the equations of its sides.

14. An equilateral triangle lying in the first quadrant has two of its vertices at $(0, 0)$ and $(a, 0)$. Write the equations of its sides.

15. Write the equation of the line through the origin which bisects that segment of the line $x + 3y = 18$ which is included between the axes.

16. Find in two different ways the equation of the locus of points equidistant from $(-2, 5)$ and $(6, 1)$.

17. Work Exercises 8 and 9, page 9, in a different way.

18. Write the equations of the two diagonals of the square two of whose opposite vertices are $(-3, 1)$ and $(5, -1)$.

19. Write the equations of the two diagonals of the rectangle three of whose vertices are $(-2, \frac{5}{2})$, $(3, -\frac{5}{2})$, and $(7, \frac{3}{2})$.

20. Write the equations of the sides of the square in Exercise 18.

21. Show that the points $(3, 11)$, $(0, 4)$, $(-3, -3)$, and $(-6, -10)$ are collinear.

22. Show analytically that the locus of points equidistant from (x_1, y_1) and (x_2, y_2) is the perpendicular bisector of the segment joining the given points.

17. Equation of a line in terms of its slope and y-intercept. A line whose y-intercept is b passes through the point $(0, b)$. Hence the equation of a line with slope m and y-intercept b can be obtained by using equation (1). The equation is, therefore,

$$y - b = m(x - 0), \quad \text{or} \quad y = mx + b.$$

The latter equation puts in evidence the slope m and the y-intercept b.

18. Equation of a line in terms of its intercepts on both axes. If the x-intercept is a and the y-intercept is b, the line passes through the two points $(a, 0)$ and $(0, b)$. Hence its equation is

$$y - b = -\frac{b}{a}(x - 0), \quad \text{or} \quad bx + ay = ab.$$

Dividing by ab, we have

$$\frac{x}{a} + \frac{y}{b} = 1.$$

This equation puts in evidence the intercepts a and b.

19. Theorem. *Every straight line can be represented by a first degree equation in two variables in rectangular coördinates; and conversely, every first degree equation in two variables in rectangular coördinates represents a straight line.*

A line is determined by a point on it and by its direction through the point. If the line is parallel to the y-axis, it can be represented by an equation of the form $x = a$, which is of the first degree. If the line is not parallel to the y-axis, a point on it and its direction are sufficient to enable us to find its equation by the method of Sec. 14. We have seen that the equation so derived is of the first degree. Hence the first part of the theorem is proved.

The general equation of the first degree in two variables is

$$Ax + By + C = 0,$$

where A, B, and C are constants. If $B \neq 0$ the equation can be written in the form

$$y = mx + b,$$

where $m = -A/B$ and $b = -C/B$. Transposing b and dividing by x, we have

$$\frac{y - b}{x} = m. \qquad (3)$$

From the figure we see that equation (3) expresses the fact that the line joining the point (x, y) to the point $(0, b)$ has the constant slope m. This is true when, and only when, the point (x, y) lies on a straight line through $(0, b)$ with slope m.

If $B=0$ the equation becomes

$$x = k,$$

where $k = -C/A$, and this is true when, and only when, the

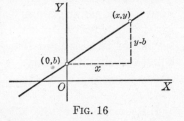

Fig. 16

point (x, y) lies on a line parallel to the y-axis and distant k units from it. Hence every first degree equation in two variables represents a straight line. Since the equation $Ax + By + C = 0$ represents a straight line, it is called a **linear equation**.

20. Reduction of the general equation to the slope and y-intercept form, and to the intercept form. It is often desirable to reduce an equation of the form $Ax + By + C = 0$ to the form $y = mx + b$, because this latter form readily shows the slope m and the y-intercept b of the line. Thus the equation
$$2x + 5y - 15 = 0$$
when solved for y becomes
$$y = -\tfrac{2}{5}x + 3.$$
This equation represents a line with slope $-\tfrac{2}{5}$ and with y-intercept 3.

To reduce an equation of the form $Ax + By + C = 0$ to the intercept form, solve for the intercepts directly from the equation and substitute in the intercept form
$$\frac{x}{a} + \frac{y}{b} = 1.$$
Thus the line whose equation is
$$2x + 5y - 15 = 0$$
has x-intercept $a = \tfrac{15}{2}$ and y-intercept $b = 3$. The intercept form of the equation is, therefore,
$$\frac{x}{\frac{15}{2}} + \frac{y}{3} = 1.$$

21. Point of intersection of two straight lines. The coördinates of the point of intersection of two straight lines must satisfy the equation of each line. Hence the point of intersection of two straight lines can be found by solving their equations simultaneously.

EXERCISES

1. Reduce each of the following equations to the slope and y-intercept form. Determine the slope and y-intercept and draw each line.

(a) $3x + 4y = 12$.   (c) $2y + 3x + 2 = 0$.
(b) $5x - y = 10$.   (d) $x - 3y = 0$.

2. Reduce equations (a), (b), and (c) in Exercise 1 to the intercept form. Why cannot (d) be reduced to the intercept form?

3. Show that the following lines form the sides of a parallelogram: $2x + 3y - 10 = 0, 2x - 10y + 29 = 0, 2x + 3y + 3 = 0,$ and $x - 5y - 5 = 0.$

4. Show that the following lines form the sides of a rectangle: $5x - 2y + 10 = 0,\ 2x + 5y + 4 = 0,\ 10x - 4y - 67 = 0,$ and $2x + 5y - 25 = 0.$

5. Find the acute angle of intersection between the lines of the following pairs:

(a) $x + 3y - 1 = 0$ and $2x - 4y + 5 = 0.$
(b) $x + y = 1$ and $(2 + \sqrt{3})x - y = 1.$

6. Find the angles of the parallelogram in Exercise 3.

7. Find the vertices of the

(a) parallelogram in Exercise 3.
(b) rectangle in Exercise 4.

8. Write the equations of the two lines through (4, 5) parallel and perpendicular, respectively, to the line $3x + 7y = 9.$

9. Find the shortest distance from the line

(a) $3x + 4y = 25$ to the origin.
(b) $x - 3y = 15$ to (1, 2).

10. Find the point on the line $x - 2y + 5 = 0$ equidistant from $(-1, 2)$ and $(7, -4).$

11. How far must each of the nonparallel sides of the trapezoid whose vertices are $(-3, -4)$, $(-1, 2)$, $(8, 5)$, and $(12, 1)$ be extended to intersect?

12. The diameter of a circle lies on the line $4x - 3y = 17$ and has for one end the point whose abscissa is 5. Find the other end if the circle passes through $(7, -3).$

13. Two opposite vertices of a square are $(-3, 2)$ and $(1, -6).$ Find the other two vertices.

14. Show that the lines $3x - 2y + 3 = 0, 5x + y - 8 = 0,$ and $x - 4y + 11 = 0$ are concurrent (intersect in a common point).

15. The vertices of a triangle are $(-5, 3)$, $(5, -3)$, and $(7, 3).$

(a) Write the equations of the medians and show that these lines intersect in a common point (centroid).

(b) Write the equations of the perpendicular bisectors of the sides and show that these lines intersect in a common point (circumcenter).

(c) Write the equations of the perpendiculars through the vertices upon the opposite sides and show that these lines intersect in a common point (orthocenter).

(d) Show that the centroid, circumcenter, and orthocenter of (a), (b), and (c), respectively, are collinear.

16. Show that the equation $A_1x + B_1y + C_1 = 0$ and the equation $A_2x + B_2y + C_2 = 0$ represent lines that are

(a) parallel if $A_1/A_2 = B_1/B_2$;
(b) perpendicular if $A_1A_2 + B_1B_2 = 0$;
(c) coincident if $A_1/A_2 = B_1/B_2 = C_1/C_2$.

17. Show that the equation of the line through the point (x_1, y_1) (a) parallel to the line $ax + by = c$ is $ax + by = ax_1 + by_1$; (b) perpendicular to the line $ax + by = c$ is $bx - ay = bx_1 - ay_1$.

22. Normal equation of a line. The normal equation of a line is the equation in terms of the perpendicular distance to the line from the origin and

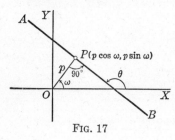

the positive angle which that perpendicular makes with the positive end of the x-axis. The distance measured from the origin to the line will be considered positive. In the figure let $p = OP$ be the perpendicular distance from the origin to the line, and let ω be the angle which OP makes with the positive end of the x-axis. The coördinates of the point of intersection P of OP with the line AB are $(p \cos \omega, p \sin \omega)$. The inclination angle θ is equal to $90° + \omega$, and hence the slope m may be written

$$m = \tan \theta = \tan (90° + \omega) = -\cot \omega.$$

The equation of the line AB is (see Sec. 14)

$$y - p \sin \omega = -\cot \omega(x - p \cos \omega).$$

Replacing $\cot \omega$ by $\cos \omega/\sin \omega$, we can reduce the equation to

$$x \cos \omega + y \sin \omega = p(\sin^2 \omega + \cos^2 \omega) = p,$$

or

$$x \cos \omega + y \sin \omega - p = 0.$$

This equation is called the **normal equation of a straight line.**

In case the line crosses a quadrant other than the first, a similar argument leads to an equation of the same form.

EXAMPLE. Write the normal equations of the two lines each of which is distant 5 units from the origin and has an inclination angle of 45°.

Since the inclination angle of each line is 45°, the lines are parallel, and for the line AB, ω is 135°, and for the line CD, ω is 315°. The equations are

$$[AB] \ x \cos 135° + y \sin 135° - 5 = 0$$

and $$[CD] \ x \cos 315° + y \sin 315° - 5 = 0,$$

or $$[AB] - \frac{\sqrt{2}}{2}x + \frac{\sqrt{2}}{2}y - 5 = 0$$

and $$[CD] \ \frac{\sqrt{2}}{2}x - \frac{\sqrt{2}}{2}y - 5 = 0.$$

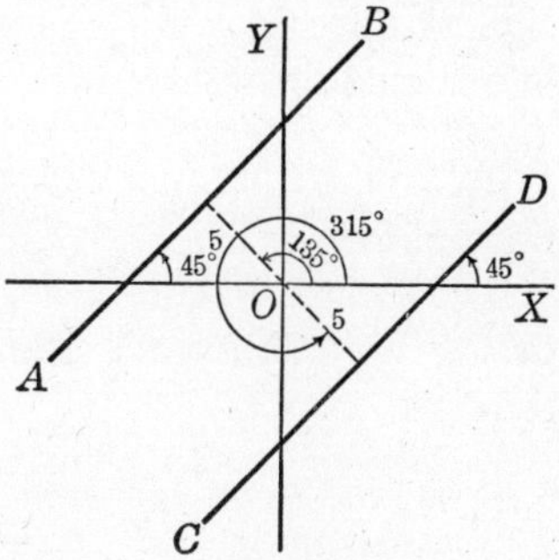

FIG. 18

23. Reduction of the general first degree equation to the normal form. If the general equation of a line,

$$Ax + By + C = 0,$$

and the normal equation,

$$x \cos \omega + y \sin \omega - p = 0,$$

represent the same line, it is possible to multiply one equation by a constant such that the two equations become identical, for this is essentially the significance of Exercise 16 c on page 28. Let us multiply the first equation by k, where k is chosen so that

$$kA = \cos \omega, \quad kB = \sin \omega, \quad \text{and} \quad kC = -p.$$

Squaring the first two of these equations and adding, we have $$k^2(A^2 + B^2) = \cos^2 \omega + \sin^2 \omega = 1.$$

Hence $$k = \frac{1}{\pm \sqrt{A^2 + B^2}}.$$

Multiplying the general equation by this value of k, we obtain the normal equation

$$\frac{Ax}{\pm\sqrt{A^2 + B^2}} + \frac{By}{\pm\sqrt{A^2 + B^2}} + \frac{C}{\pm\sqrt{A^2 + B^2}} = 0,$$

where the sign before the radical must be chosen opposite to the sign of C in order to agree with the normal form. In case $C = 0$, the sign of the radical is chosen the same as the sign of B, so that $\sin \omega$ is positive, that is, so that ω shall be less than 180°.

EXAMPLE. Reduce the equation $2x - 3y + 6 = 0$ to the normal form.

The constant multiplier which will reduce the equation to the normal form is found to be $1/(-\sqrt{13})$. Hence the required form is

$$-\frac{2x}{\sqrt{13}} + \frac{3y}{\sqrt{13}} - \frac{6}{\sqrt{13}} = 0.$$

From this equation we see that for the given line

$$\cos \omega = -2/\sqrt{13}, \quad \sin \omega = 3/\sqrt{13}, \quad \text{and} \quad p = 6/\sqrt{13}.$$

24. Distance from a line to a point. The distance from the line AB (Fig. 19) to the point (x_1, y_1) can be found in the following manner. The normal equation of the line AB is

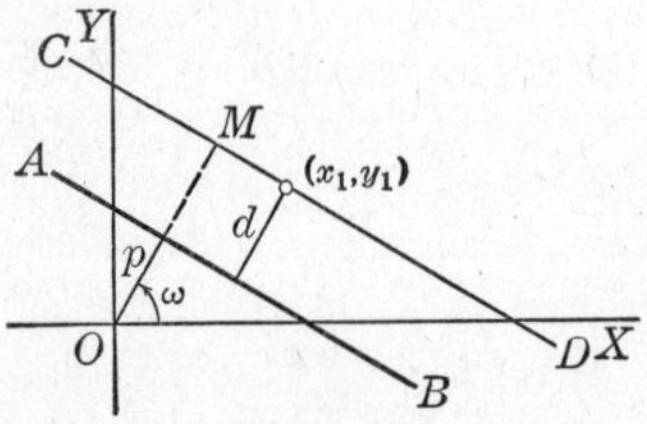

FIG. 19

$$x \cos \omega + y \sin \omega - p = 0.$$

If a line CD is drawn through the point (x_1, y_1) parallel to AB, its equation will evidently be

$$x \cos \omega + y \sin \omega - p_1 = 0,$$

where $p_1 = OM$. But $OM = p + d$, where d is the distance from the line AB to the point (x_1, y_1). Since the point (x_1, y_1) is on the line CD,

$$x_1 \cos \omega + y_1 \sin \omega - (p + d) = 0,$$

or

$$d = x_1 \cos \omega + y_1 \sin \omega - p.$$

Therefore, the distance from a line to a point can be found by writing the equation of the line in normal form and substituting in the left member of the equation the coördinates of the point. The result is the distance from the line to the point, and is zero only if the point is on the line. If the point (x_1, y_1) lies on the opposite side of the line AB from the origin, the distance d is positive (note positive sense of direction adopted in Sec. 22), and if the point lies on the same side of the line as the origin, the distance d is negative.

EXAMPLE. Find the distance from the line $7x + y - 10 = 0$ to the point $(3, 4)$.

Reducing the equation to the normal form, we have

$$\frac{7x + y - 10}{5\sqrt{2}} = 0.$$

Substituting in the left member the coördinates of the given point, we have

$$d = \frac{7 \cdot 3 + 1 \cdot 4 - 10}{5\sqrt{2}} = \frac{15}{5\sqrt{2}} = \frac{3\sqrt{2}}{2},$$

the required distance. Since the distance is positive, the given point $(3, 4)$ is on the opposite side of the line from the origin.

25. Equation of the bisector of an angle. EXAMPLE. Find the equations of the bisectors of the angles formed by the lines $3x + 4y + 10 = 0$ and $5x - 12y - 12 = 0$.

We make use of the fact that the bisector of an angle is the locus of points equidistant from the sides of the angle. From the figure we have

$$FP = EP$$

and $\qquad MP' = -NP'$,

where FP and EP have the same signs and MP' and NP'

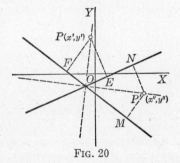

FIG. 20

have opposite signs, since P is on the same side of each line as the origin and P' is not. But

$$FP = \frac{3\,x' + 4\,y' + 10}{-5},$$

$$EP = \frac{5\,x' - 12\,y' - 12}{13},$$

$$MP' = \frac{3\,x'' + 4\,y'' + 10}{-5}, \quad \text{and} \quad NP' = \frac{5\,x'' - 12\,y'' - 12}{13}.$$

Hence the locus of P is

$$\frac{3\,x' + 4\,y' + 10}{-5} = \frac{5\,x' - 12\,y' - 12}{13},$$

and the locus of P' is

$$\frac{3\,x'' + 4\,y'' + 10}{-5} = -\frac{5\,x'' - 12\,y'' - 12}{13}.$$

Clearing of fractions, reducing, and omitting prime marks, we have as the equations of the two bisectors

$$32\,x - 4\,y + 35 = 0 \quad \text{and} \quad 7\,x + 56\,y + 95 = 0.$$

It will be observed that these lines have slopes which are negative reciprocals, and the lines are, therefore, perpendicular. This was proved in elementary geometry and gives a check on our work.

EXERCISES

1. Draw each of the lines for which the following conditions are given and write its equation in normal form:

(a) $\omega = 45°$, $p = 2$.   (d) $\omega = 5\,\pi/4$, $p = 1$.
(b) $\omega = 120°$, $p = 3$.   (e) $\omega = \pi/6$, $p = 0$.
(c) $\omega = 180°$, $p = 5$.   (f) $\omega = \pi/2$, $p = 10$.

2. Reduce each of the following equations to the normal form, determine ω and p, and draw each line:

(a) $3\,x + 4\,y - 10 = 0$.   (c) $x + y + 8 = 0$.
(b) $5\,x - 12\,y + 39 = 0$.   (d) $\sqrt{3}\,x - y = 0$.

3. Derive the normal form from the intercept form of the equation of the straight line.

4. Show that the distance d from the line $Ax + By + C = 0$ to the point (x_1, y_1) is $d = \dfrac{Ax_1 + By_1 + C}{\pm \sqrt{A^2 + B^2}}$.

5. Find the distance from the origin to the line $y = mx + b$ in terms of m and b (a) by using the normal form; (b) by trigonometry directly from a figure.

6. Find the distance from the line $4x + 3y - 13 = 0$ to each of the following points:

(a) $(2, 5)$; (b) $(-2, 2)$; (c) $(4, -1)$; (d) $(0, 0)$.

7. Work Exercise 9 (a) and (b), page 27, by the method of Sec. 24.

8. The line $8x + 15y + 1 = 0$ is tangent to a circle whose center is $(3, 4)$. Find the length of the radius.

9. Find the distance from the line

(a) $x + y = 0$ to $(2, 1)$.   (b) $x - y = 0$ to $(2, 1)$.

10. Show that $(2, 6)$ and $(3, 10)$ lie on opposite sides of the line $24x - 7y - 5 = 0$.

11. Find the distance between the parallel lines

(a) $y = 10 - 2x$ and $y = 15 - 2x$.
(b) $x - 3y + 20 = 0$ and $x - 3y - 10 = 0$.

12. The base of a triangle is 10 units in length and lies along the line $9x + 40y - 36 = 0$. Find its area if its vertex lies on the line $9x + 40y - 200 = 0$.

13. Find the equation of the locus of points numerically equidistant from the parallel lines in each set of Exercise 11.

14. The distance between two parallel lines is 6. The line $12x + 5y - 39 = 0$ is parallel to them and midway between them. Write the equations of the two lines.

15. Find the points equidistant from $(0, 10)$ and $(8, 6)$ and at the distances ± 4 from the line $4x + 3y - 10 = 0$.

16. Find the length of each of the three altitudes of the triangle whose vertices are $(2, 5)$, $(2, -5)$, and $(10, 1)$.

17. Find the area of the triangle whose vertices are $(0, -2)$, $(7, -1)$, and $(5, 3)$.

18. Find the equations of the bisectors of the angles between the lines $x + 3y - 6 = 0$ and $6x + 2y - 3 = 0$.

19. Find the equations of the bisectors of the angles of the triangle formed by the lines $3x + 4y - 12 = 0$, $4x - 3y + 9 = 0$, and $8x - 15y - 54 = 0$, and show that these bisectors are concurrent.

20. Find the radius of the inscribed circle of the triangle in Exercise 19.

21. In Exercise 19, show that the bisectors of the right angle and of the opposite exterior angles are concurrent.

26. Constants in the equation of a straight line. The general equation

$$Ax + By + C = 0$$

has but two essential constants, since if any one of the constants A, B, or C, say A, is different from zero we may divide by it, thus reducing the equation to

$$x + dy + e = 0,$$

where $d = B/A$ and $e = C/A$. The constants we have used are five in number, the slope m, the intercepts a and b on the axes, the perpendicular distance p from the origin, and the direction angle ω of the perpendicular.

Two geometric conditions determine a line, such as two points, or a point and a direction. Two constants are sufficient to make an equation satisfy two conditions. For example, if we want the line $y = mx + b$ to pass through the point (3, 2), we have

$$2 = 3m + b,$$

since the coördinates of a point on a line satisfy the equation of the line. *Thus to the geometric condition that the point is on the line corresponds the algebraic condition $2 = 3m + b$, showing a relation between the constants.* A second geometric condition will give a second algebraic equation corresponding to that condition. From our study of simultaneous equations in algebra we recall that two equations are sufficient to determine two unknowns. *Hence we may put as many geometric conditions on a line as there are undetermined constants in the equation of a line, namely, two.*

27. Families of lines. When we consider the equation $y = 2x + b$, we see that it represents a line with slope 2 for each value of b. Giving particular values to b, we have parallel lines with different y-intercepts. The figure is drawn for $b = -2, -1, 0, 1$, and 2. Such a system of lines, depending upon an arbitrary constant, is called a **family of lines**. The arbitrary constant is frequently called a **parameter**. If we want the line of this family which passes through some given point, for example $(3, 10)$, we determine the parameter b so that the coördinates $(3, 10)$ satisfy the equation. Substituting these coördinates in the equation $y = 2x + b$, we find $b = 4$. Hence the desired equation is $y = 2x + 4$.

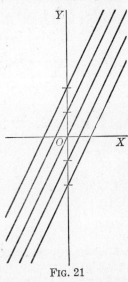

Fig. 21

Each of the type forms of the equation of the straight line represents a family of lines depending upon the parameters in it. When the parameters are given definite values, a particular member is selected from the family of lines represented by the equation with parameters. A line can be made to satisfy as many conditions as there are parameters in the type equation.

EXAMPLE 1. From the family of lines represented by the equation $y = mx + b$ select the one passing through $(3, 3)$ and $(-1, -5)$.

Since these points are on the line, the coördinates of each must satisfy the equation, and we have

$$3 = 3m + b \quad \text{and} \quad -5 = -m + b.$$

Solving simultaneously, we obtain $m = 2$ and $b = -3$. Hence $y = 2x - 3$ is the line of the family $y = mx + b$ which passes through the given points.

EXAMPLE 2. Write the equations of all lines through (4, 3) each of which has the product of the intercepts on the axes equal to 54.

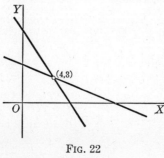

FIG. 22

Since we need the intercepts on the axes we use the equation

$$x/a + y/b = 1.$$

The point (4, 3) is on the line; hence

$$4/a + 3/b = 1.$$

From the statement of the problem

$$ab = 54.$$

The simultaneous solutions of these equations are $a = 6$, $b = 9$ and $a = 12$, $b = 4\frac{1}{2}$. If these values are substituted in the equation $x/a + y/b = 1$ in turn, we have the required equations

$$3x + 2y = 18 \quad \text{and} \quad 3x + 8y = 36.$$

EXERCISES

1. Draw several members of each of the following families of lines and determine the common property possessed by each family:

(a) $y = 3x + b$.

(b) $y = mx + 3$.

(c) $x = k$.

(d) $\dfrac{x}{a} + \dfrac{y}{3} = 1$.

(e) $x \cos \pi/3 + y \sin \pi/3 - p = 0$.

(f) $y = mx$.

(g) $y - 2 = m(x - 3)$.

(h) $x \cos \omega + y \sin \omega - 6 = 0$.

2. Write the equations of the families of lines parallel and perpendicular, respectively, to the line $3x + 8y = 0$. Select the member from each family which passes through (4, 1).

3. Select that member of the family of lines $y = mx + 5$ which

(a) passes through $(-1, 6)$;

(b) has its x-intercept equal to its y-intercept;

(c) is 4 units distant from the origin;

(d) is parallel to the x-axis;

(e) is parallel to the y-axis.

4. Write the equation of the family of lines perpendicular to the line segment joining $(-3, 1)$ and $(7, -3)$, and select the member of this family which bisects this segment.

5. Write the equation of the family of lines each of which has its x-intercept twice its y-intercept, and select the member of this family which passes through $(5, 3)$.

6. Select those members of the family of lines $x + cy = 4$ which intersect the line $x - 2y - 6 = 0$ at an angle of (a) $45°$; (b) $90°$.

7. Write the equation of the family of lines tangent to the circle of radius 5 with center at the origin and select that member of this family which is tangent to the circle at $(4, 3)$.

8. Select those members of the family in Exercise 7 which are perpendicular to the special member found in that exercise.

9. Write the equations of all lines through $(2, 3)$ each of which has the sum of its intercepts on the axes equal to 10.

10. Write the equations of all lines through $(5, 1)$ each of which has the product of its intercepts on the axes equal to 20.

11. Write the equation of the line through $(2, 4)$ which forms with the coördinate axes a right triangle of area (a) 25 sq. units; (b) 16 sq. units; (c) 12 sq. units.

12. Write the equations of the line through $(-6, 2)$ and $(4, 7)$, using in turn each of the following forms:

(a) $y = mx + b$;   (b) $\dfrac{x}{a} + \dfrac{y}{b} = 1$;   (c) $x \cos \omega + y \sin \omega - p = 0$.

28. Lines through the point of intersection of two given lines. The coördinates of the point of intersection of the two lines

$$a_1 x + b_1 y + c_1 = 0 \quad \text{and} \quad a_2 x + b_2 y + c_2 = 0$$

satisfy the equation

$$(a_1 x + b_1 y + c_1) + k(a_2 x + b_2 y + c_2) = 0 \qquad (4)$$

for every value of k, since the substitution of the coördinates of the point of intersection makes each expression in parenthesis equal to zero. Equation (4) is of the first degree and, therefore, represents a straight line. Hence equation (4) represents a straight line through the intersection of the first two lines for every value of k. By the proper choice of the parameter k this line can be made to satisfy one more condition.

EXAMPLE. Find the equation of the line through the intersection of the lines $2x + 3y - 9 = 0$ and $x + 2y - 7 = 0$ and with slope $-\frac{1}{3}$.

The equation

$$2x + 3y - 9 + k(x + 2y - 7) = 0$$

represents a family of lines through the intersection of the given lines. The slope of any member of the family of lines in terms of k is

$$m = -\frac{2 + k}{3 + 2k}.$$

This value for m is readily found if the equation is reduced to the form $y = mx + b$. Since the slope of the line whose equation is desired is $-\frac{1}{3}$, we let

$$-\frac{2 + k}{3 + 2k} = -\frac{1}{3}.$$

This gives $k = -3$. Substituting the value of k in the equation representing the family of lines and collecting terms, we have the required equation,

$$x + 3y - 12 = 0.$$

EXERCISES

Work the following exercises without finding the point of intersection of the given lines.

1. Write the equation of the line (or lines) through the intersection of the given lines in the example of Sec. 28 which

    (a) passes through $(5, 7)$;
    (b) has its x-intercept equal to three times its y-intercept;
    (c) is distant 3 units from the origin.

2. Write the equation of the line through the intersection of the lines $x + 5y - 6 = 0$ and $2x - y + 3 = 0$ and through the origin.

3. Write the equation of the line through the intersection of the lines $x + 2y - 5 = 0$ and $3x - 5y + 7 = 0$ and parallel to a line with slope 5.

4. Write the equation of the line through the intersection of the lines $2x - y + 7 = 0$ and $x + 5y - 3 = 0$ perpendicular to the first of the given lines.

5. Write the equation of the line through the intersection of the lines $4x + y - 4 = 0$ and $3x - 8y - 10 = 0$ and having its (a) x-intercept equal to 2; (b) y-intercept equal to -2; (c) distance from the origin equal to $\sqrt{2}$.

6. Write the equations of all the lines through the intersection of the lines $x + y - 8 = 0$ and $2x - y + 2 = 0$ each of which forms with the axes a right triangle of area 27 sq. units.

7. Find the equations of all the lines passing through the intersection of the lines $x - 3y + 1 = 0$ and $2x + 5y - 9 = 0$ and having their distance from the origin (a) 2 units; (b) $\sqrt{5}$ units; (c) 3 units.

8. Find the equation of the line through the intersection of the lines $2x + y - 8 = 0$ and $4x - 3y - 6 = 0$ and through (a) $(-1, 10)$; (b) $(6, 6)$; (c) $(3, 2)$.

MISCELLANEOUS EXERCISES

1. Determine a, b, m, p, and ω for the line $11x - 2y + 25 = 0$.

2. Find the intercepts on the axes of the line through $(-\frac{1}{3}, 3)$ and $(2, -\frac{1}{2})$.

3. Find the foot of the perpendicular drawn from the origin to the line $x + 3y = 20$.

4. The x- and y-intercepts of a line are -5 and 1 respectively. Find the point on this line equidistant from $(-1, -4)$ and $(11, -10)$.

5. Find the point equidistant from $(1, 6)$, $(9, 0)$, and $(-3, -6)$.

6. Determine a so that the points $(-5, -6)$, $(1, 4)$, and $(a, 9)$ shall be collinear.

7. Determine c so that the lines $x - y + 2 = 0$, $2x - 3y + 7 = 0$, and $3x + 2y + c = 0$ shall be concurrent.

8. Show that each member of the family $x - 2y + c_1 = 0$ intersects every member of the family $x + 3y + c_2 = 0$ at an angle of $45°$.

9. Two vertices of an equilateral triangle lying in the first quadrant are $(a, 0)$ and $(0, a)$. Write the equations of its three sides.

10. The lines $3x + 4y + 18 = 0$ and $3x + 4y - 12 = 0$ are parallel tangents to a certain circle. What is the length of the diameter of the circle?

11. The equations of two adjacent sides of a parallelogram are $x + 2y - 4 = 0$ and $3x + y + 3 = 0$. One vertex is $(8, -7)$. Write the equations of the other two sides and the two diagonals.

12. Two sides and one diagonal of a parallelogram are the lines $3x - 8y + 4 = 0$, $3x - 8y - 24 = 0$, and $x + 2y + 6 = 0$, respectively. The other diagonal passes through $(1, 0)$. Find the four vertices.

13. Find the equations of the bisectors of the angles of the parallelogram whose sides are the lines $3x + 4y - 11 = 0$, $3x + 4y + 17 = 0$, $5x - 12y + 19 = 0$, and $5x - 12y - 93 = 0$, and show that these bisectors inclose a rectangle.

14. The equations of the two legs of an isosceles triangle are $2y = 7$ and $8x + 6y = 45$. Find the length of the base if its midpoint is $(1, -\frac{1}{2})$.

15. The equations of the two legs of an isosceles triangle are $7x - y + 3 = 0$ and $x + y - 3 = 0$. Find the length of the base if it passes through $(1, -10)$.

16. Write the equations of all lines through $(2, 6)$ each of which is 6 units distant from the origin.

17. Write the equations of all lines through $(2, 7)$ each of which has the length of its segment included between the axes equal to $5\sqrt{2}$.

18. Write the equation of the line through the intersection of the lines $x + y + 3 = 0$ and $3x + y + 5 = 0$ and through the intersection of the lines $x - y - 4 = 0$ and $2x - y - 9 = 0$ without finding the point of intersection of either pair of lines.

19. A pole 50 ft. long leans away from a vertical pole 60 ft. long. The bases of the poles are 30 ft. apart and the leaning pole makes an angle $\tan^{-1} \frac{24}{7}$ with the ground (horizontal). Find the distance from the base of the vertical pole to the point where the line through the tops of the poles strikes the ground.

20. Generalize Exercise 15 (a), (b), (c), and (d), page 27, for any triangle. (Note there is no loss of generality in choosing for the vertices $(0, 0)$, $(a, 0)$, and (b, c).)

21. Show analytically that the perpendicular distance from the vertex of the right angle of a right triangle upon the hypotenuse is equal to the product of the lengths of the two legs divided by the length of the hypotenuse.

22. Show analytically that the two lines drawn from a vertex of a parallelogram to the midpoints of the opposite sides trisect a diagonal of the parallelogram.

23. A point moves so that the sum of the squares of its distances from two vertices of an equilateral triangle is equal to twice the square of its distance from the third vertex. Show analytically that its locus is a straight line parallel to a side of the triangle and passing through the point of intersection of the medians.

24. Write the equation of the line through $P(x_1, y_1)$ perpendicular to the line $Ax + By + C = 0$. Find the intersection, N, of this perpendicular with the given line and thence find the length of the segment NP by Sec. 6. Compare with Exercise 4, page 33.

25. Show that the equation of the line through the points (x_1, y_1) and (x_2, y_2) is given by

$$\begin{vmatrix} x & y & 1 \\ x_1 & y_1 & 1 \\ x_2 & y_2 & 1 \end{vmatrix} = 0.$$

(*Hint.* See Exercise 15, page 18.)

CHAPTER III

EQUATION AND LOCUS

29. Graph of an equation. In Chapter II we have seen that every equation of the first degree in two variables has a straight line associated with it, and conversely. We shall now consider equations of higher degree than the first and their corresponding geometric loci. Consider, for example, the equation $4y = x^3$. It is evidently satisfied by infinitely many pairs of values of x and y. Writing the equation in the form $y = x^3/4$ and assigning values to x, we can easily obtain corresponding values for y. A few of these pairs of values are

$x =$	-4	-3	-2	-1	0	1	2	3	4
$y =$	-16	$-6\frac{3}{4}$	-2	$-\frac{1}{4}$	0	$\frac{1}{4}$	2	$6\frac{3}{4}$	16

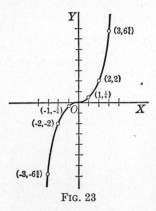

Fig. 23

Using the pairs of values of x and y found above, we can plot the points shown in Fig. 23. We observe that these points do not lie on a straight line but appear to lie on a smooth curve, as shown in the figure. If additional pairs of values of x and y are found and the corresponding points plotted, a more accurate curve can be drawn. It should be observed that the curve recedes indefinitely far from the axes in the first and third quadrants. The curve recedes more rapidly from the x-axis than from the y-axis since the ordinate y varies as the cube of the abscissa x.

42

Definition. *The locus or graph of an equation in two variables is the curve* * *containing all the points, and only the points, whose coördinates satisfy the equation.*

Assuming that the curve shown in Fig. 23 satisfies the conditions of the definition, we call it the graph of the equation $4y = x^3$.

As a second illustration consider the equation $xy = 1$. Writing the equation in the form $y = 1/x$ and assigning values to x, we find corresponding values of y and tabulate them as follows:

$x =$	1	2	3	4	$\frac{1}{2}$	$\frac{1}{3}$	$\frac{1}{4}$	-1	-2	-3	-4	$-\frac{1}{2}$	$-\frac{1}{3}$	$-\frac{1}{4}$
$y =$	1	$\frac{1}{2}$	$\frac{1}{3}$	$\frac{1}{4}$	2	3	4	-1	$-\frac{1}{2}$	$-\frac{1}{3}$	$-\frac{1}{4}$	-2	-3	-4

Having plotted these points, the student may be puzzled as to how to join them. As in the preceding example the points are confined to the first and third quadrants, but it should be noted that the value $x = 0$ must be excluded, since for the value $x = 0$ there is no corre-sponding value of y. The curve, therefore, does not cut the y-axis, and hence is composed of two separate branches, as shown in the figure.

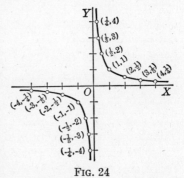

Fig. 24

Although $x = 0$ is excluded, we observe that as x approaches zero through positive values, y increases indefinitely and the branch in the first quadrant recedes indefinitely from the x-axis and approaches the upward extension of the y-axis. Also as x increases indefinitely through positive values, y decreases and approaches zero. The graph, therefore, recedes indefinitely from the y-axis and approaches the positive ex-

---

* The word "curve" used in a general sense includes the straight line. The definition of graph in Chapter II is a special case of the general definition here.

tension of the x-axis. A similar discussion shows that the branch in the third quadrant extends indefinitely toward the negative extensions of the x- and y-axes.

EXERCISES

Draw the graphs of the following equations:

1. $2\,y = x^2$.
2. $2\,y = x^2 + 2$.
3. $y = x^2 - 3\,x$.
4. $y = 3\,x - x^2$.
5. $y^2 = 4\,x$.
6. $y^2 = -4\,x$.

7. $y = x^3$.
8. $y^3 = x$.
9. $y = x^4$.
10. $4\,y = x^4$.
11. $y^2 = x^3$.
12. $y^3 = x^2$.

13. $xy = 9$.
14. $xy = -9$.
15. $x^2 y = 10$.
16. $xy^2 = 10$.
17. $x^2 + y^2 = 25$.
18. $x^2 - y^2 = 25$.

19. $y = x^3 - x$.
20. $y = x^4 - x^2$.

21. $y^2 - 2\,y - x - 3 = 0$.
22. $x^2 - 6\,x - 3\,y + 9 = 0$.

30. The two fundamental problems of a first course in analytic geometry. In the preceding chapter we studied two types of problems: (1) given the equation of a line to locate the corresponding line; (2) given the line to find the corresponding equation. We are now interested in considering the similar problems for equations and loci in general:

1. *Given an equation to find the corresponding locus or graph.*
2. *Given a locus to find the corresponding equation.*

This second problem frequently takes the form of finding an equation whose graph approximately fits a set of points given by some sort of observed data. This phase of the second problem is not treated in this book. See Mason and Hazard's "Analytic Geometry," Chapter X.

31. Remarks. A curve representing an equation can be drawn fairly accurately if a sufficient number of points are plotted. In many cases, however, so many points are required to furnish an accurate conception of the curve that the point method becomes very laborious. Furthermore, the point method in itself furnishes little or no information concerning some of the important properties of the curve. There are certain properties, however, easily detected from the equation, which if discovered and used will enable one to draw the curve with a minimum amount of point plotting. Some of these properties are discussed in the sections following.

32. Intercepts. The intercepts of a curve are the directed distances from the origin to the points where the curve crosses or touches the axes. To find the x-intercept, let $y = 0$ in the equation of the curve and solve for x. Similarly, to find the y-intercept, let $x = 0$ and solve for y.

33. Symmetry. Two points are symmetric with respect to a line if that line is the perpendicular bisector of the line joining the two points. Two points are symmetric with respect to a third point if that third point is the midpoint of the line joining the first two points. It follows immediately from these definitions that the

point (x, y) is symmetric to $\begin{cases} (x, -y) \text{ with respect to the} \\ \quad x\text{-axis.} \\ (-x, y) \text{ with respect to the} \\ \quad y\text{-axis.} \\ (-x, -y) \text{ with respect to the} \\ \quad \text{origin.} \end{cases}$

A curve is symmetric with respect to a line or with respect to a point if the symmetric point of each point on the curve is also a point on the curve. The curve will be symmetric with respect to the x-axis if for each point (x, y) on the curve the symmetric point $(x, -y)$ is also on the curve. For example, this is true of the curve whose equation is $x + y^2 = 3$. The equation must be such that the substitution of $-y$ for y does not change its form. This will be true if y occurs in the equation to even powers only.

Similarly, a curve is symmetric with respect to the y-axis if x occurs to even powers only.

A curve is symmetric with respect to the origin if the substitution of $-x$ for x and of $-y$ for y does not change the form of the equation of the curve. Thus the curves of the illustrative examples in Sec. 29 are symmetric with respect to the origin. Symmetry with respect to both axes implies symmetry with respect to the origin, but not conversely.

34. Extent. Our graphical scheme represents points with real coördinates only. Hence values of x must be excluded for which y is imaginary and values of y must be excluded for which x is imaginary. Such cases will arise if in expressing one variable in terms of the other we have a negative radicand and an even root index. Thus if $y = 2\,ax + \sqrt{9 - x^2}$, we see that x cannot be greater than 3 nor less than -3 if y is to be real. Hence the curve lies between the two lines $x = \pm\,3$. And if $x = \sqrt{y - 5}$, it is obvious that y cannot be less than 5 if x is to be real. Hence the curve lies above the line $y = 5$.

The student should solve for x and y in turn and see if the curve is limited in extent.

35. Examples of graphing. EXAMPLE 1. Draw the curve $y^2 = 4\,x + 4$.

Since y occurs to an even power only there is symmetry with respect to the x-axis. There is no symmetry with re-

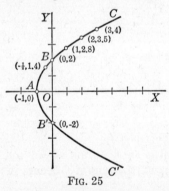

FIG. 25

spect to the y-axis or the origin. The intercepts are $\pm\,2$ on the y-axis and -1 on the x-axis. Solving the equation for y, we have
$$y = \pm\,2\sqrt{x + 1},$$
which shows that values of x less than -1 must be excluded, since corresponding values of y would be imaginary. Also, it is seen that y increases numerically as x increases. Hence the curve will recede from the x-axis as x increases. For $x = -\frac{1}{2}$, $y = \pm\,1.4 +$; for $x = 1$, $y = \pm\,2.8 +$; for $x = 2$, $y = \pm\,3.5 -$; for $x = 3$, $y = \pm\,4$; etc. Marking off the intercepts and plotting the points with positive ordinates, we draw a smooth curve ABC (Fig. 25) through them in the

order of increasing abscissas. The lower branch $AB'C'$ is next drawn symmetric to the branch ABC with respect to the x-axis.

It should be noticed that the double sign before the radical in the equation $y = \pm 2\sqrt{x+1}$ also indicates symmetry with respect to the x-axis, since for every value of x there are two values of y numerically equal but opposite in sign.

EXAMPLE 2. Draw the curve $4x^2 + 9y^2 = 36$.

The curve is symmetric with respect to each axis and therefore with respect to the origin. The x-intercepts are ± 3

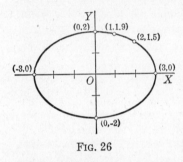

FIG. 26

and the y-intercepts are ± 2. Solving the equation for y, we have

$$y = \pm \tfrac{2}{3}\sqrt{9 - x^2}.$$

This equation shows that x cannot be numerically greater than 3. It also shows that for $x = 0$, y has its largest numerical value, namely 2, and that as x increases toward 3, y decreases numerically toward zero. For $x = 1$, $y = \pm 1.9 -$; and for $x = 2$, $y = \pm 1.5 -$. Marking off the intercepts and plotting the points which lie in the first quadrant, we draw the entire curve (Fig. 26), keeping in mind the facts of symmetry and the limitations on x and y.

EXAMPLE 3. Draw the curve $y = x^3 - 4x$.

If we replace x by $-x$ and y by $-y$ the equation becomes

$$-y = -x^3 + 4x \quad \text{or} \quad y = x^3 - 4x.$$

Hence the curve is symmetric with respect to the origin. The x-intercepts are -2, 0, and 2. The y-intercept is 0. Writing the equation in the form

$$y = (x+2)x(x-2),$$

FIG. 27

we see that for $x < -2$, y is negative since each factor in the right member of the equation is negative; for $-2 < x < 0$, y is positive; for $0 < x < 2$, y is again negative; and for $x > 2$, y is positive. With the information in regard to the change in sign of y, the intercepts, and symmetry with respect to the origin, a rough sketch of the curve can be indicated as in Fig. 27. However, if a few additional points are plotted, such as $(1, -3)$ and $(3, 15)$, a more accurate sketch is obtained (Fig. 28). And even this sketch can be further refined as more points are plotted. We are not sure, for instance, that $(1, -3)$ is the lowest point on that part of the curve, as Fig. 28 seems to indicate.

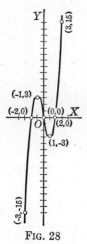

Fig. 28

EXAMPLE 4. Draw the curve
$$x^2 + y^2 - 8x = 0.$$
Solving the equation for x, we have
$$x = 4 \pm \sqrt{16 - y^2}.$$

This equation shows that the curve is symmetric with respect to the line $x = 4$, since for each value of y there are two values of x, one as much less than 4 as the other is greater than 4. The curve is also symmetric with respect to the x-axis. The curve goes through the origin and crosses the x-axis again at $x = 8$. The values of y cannot be greater than 4 nor less than -4, and the corresponding values of x lie in the interval from 0 to 8. The curve is shown in Fig. 29.

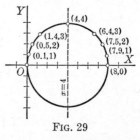

Fig. 29

The foregoing examples illustrate some of the different methods of attack upon problems that will confront the student in drawing the graphs corresponding to given equations. They do not exhaust the devices which may be used but are meant to be suggestive of types of attack to employ.

EXERCISES

Discuss and draw the graphs of the following equations:

1. $y^2 + 8x = 16$.
2. $y^2 + 4 = 4x$.
3. $x^2 + 2y = 8$.
4. $x^2 + y^2 = 20$.
5. $x^2 + 4y^2 = 16$.
6. $x^2 - 4y^2 = 16$.
7. $4y^2 - x^2 = 16$.
8. $y = x^3 + 1$.
9. $y^2 = x^3 + 1$.
10. $y = x^3 - 9x$.

11. $y = x^3 + 9x$.
12. $y = x(x+2)(x-3)$.
13. $y = x(x+2)(x-3)^2$.
14. $y = (x^2 - 1)^2$.
15. $y^2 = 9x^2 - x^4$.
16. $y^2 = 9x^4 - x^6$.
17. $y^2 = x(x-4)^2$.
18. $y^2 = x^2(4-x)$.
19. $y^3 = x + y$.
20. $y^4 = x^2 + y^2$.

In Exercises 21 and 22 solve for y in terms of x, determine a line of symmetry and draw the graph.

21. $x^2 + y^2 - 6y = 0$.
22. $y^2 - 4y - x + 3 = 0$.

23. Solve for x in terms of y, determine a line of symmetry and draw the graph: $x^2 - 4x + 4y^2 = 0$.

24. In Example 4, Sec. 35, solve for y in terms of x and draw the graph.

25. If x and y are interchanged in an equation, show that the graph of the new equation is symmetric to the graph of the first with respect to the line $y = x$.

36. Asymptotes parallel to an axis. EXAMPLE. Draw the graph of $xy + y = x$.

The curve goes through the origin. There is no symmetry with respect to the axes or the origin. Solving the equation for y, we have

$$y = \frac{x}{x+1}.$$

For $x < -1$, y is positive since both numerator and denominator are negative; for $-1 < x < 0$, y is negative; for x positive, y is positive. As x approaches -1 the numerator of the fraction approaches -1 while the denominator approaches zero. Hence the value of the fraction increases numerically without limit, that is, approaches infinity (∞). As x approaches -1 from the left, y approaches $+\infty$, and as x approaches -1 from the right, y approaches $-\infty$. As x ap-

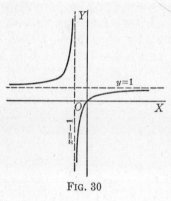

FIG. 30

proaches $+\infty$, y approaches 1 but is always less than 1 since the denominator is greater than the numerator. As x approaches $-\infty$, y approaches 1 but is always greater than 1 since the numerator is numerically greater than the denominator. The fact that the curve recedes indefinitely, and approaches the lines $x = -1$ and $y = 1$, aids in drawing the curve (Fig. 30).

Such a line as $x = -1$, or $y = 1$, in the preceding example, which the curve approaches as one of the variables approaches infinity, is called an **asymptote** of the curve. In some cases the coördinate axes are asymptotes, as in Fig. 24.

EXERCISES

Discuss and draw the graphs of the following equations:

1. $y = \dfrac{2}{x-1}$.

2. $y = \dfrac{2x}{x-1}$.

3. $x = \dfrac{3}{2+y}$.

4. $y = \dfrac{9}{(x-3)^2}$.

5. $y = \dfrac{8}{(x-2)^3}$.

6. $y = \dfrac{4}{x^2-4}$.

7. $y = \dfrac{4x}{x^2-4}$.

8. $y = \dfrac{6}{(x+2)(x-3)}$.

9. $y = \dfrac{x-1}{x+2}$.

10. $y = \dfrac{2(x-1)}{(x+2)(x-4)}$.

11. $y = \dfrac{1}{(x^2-1)^2}$.

12. $y = \dfrac{x}{(x^2-1)^2}$.

13. $y = \dfrac{4}{1 + x^2}.$

15. $y = \dfrac{2\,x^2}{x^2 + 4}.$

14. $y = \dfrac{4\,x}{1 + x^2}.$

16. $y = \dfrac{x^2 - 1}{x^2 + 1}.$

37. Graphing by factoring. If the first member of an equation $f(x,\,y) = 0$ can be factored into two or more factors, as $f(x,\,y) = f_1(x,\,y) \cdot f_2(x,\,y) = 0$, it is evident that only those points $(x,\,y)$ whose coördinates satisfy either $f_1(x,\,y) = 0$ or $f_2(x,\,y) = 0$ will lie on the locus of $f(x,\,y) = 0$. Hence the graph of $f(x,\,y) = 0$ will be made up of the graphs of $f_1(x,\,y) = 0$ and $f_2(x,\,y) = 0$.

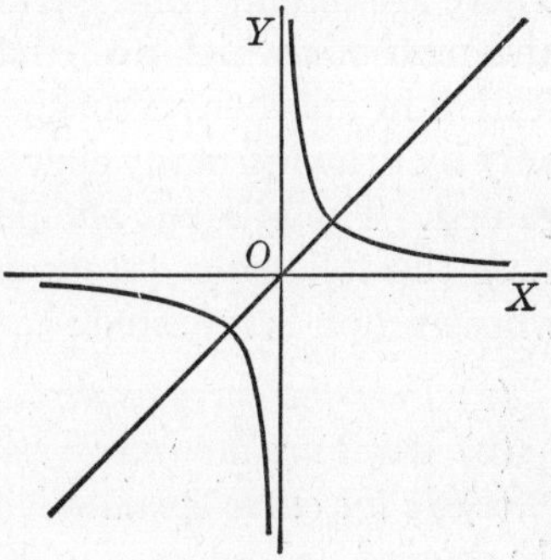

EXAMPLE. Graph
$$x^2y - xy^2 - x + y = 0.$$
Factoring, we have
$$x^2y - xy^2 - x + y$$
$$= (xy - 1)(x - y) = 0.$$

FIG. 31

Hence the required graph is made up of the graphs of the equations $xy - 1 = 0$ and $x - y = 0$. The graph of $xy - 1 = 0$ is shown in Fig. 24, and the graph of $x - y = 0$ is a line through the origin with slope 1. The complete graph is shown in Fig. 31.

38. Equation in two variables. In any equation we have graphed by plotting points we have seen that the points tend to lie on a curve rather than to cover an area. It can be proved that any equation in rectangular coördinates, $f(x,\,y) = 0$, represents a curve, isolated points, or no real locus. The proof is beyond the scope of this book.

Some equations are satisfied by the coördinates of only one point, or of a finite number of points, and their graphs are called point loci. The equation $x^2 + y^2 = 0$ is satisfied by the coördinates of the point $(0,\,0)$ only. The equation $(x^2 - 1)^2 + (y^2 - 1)^2 = 0$ is satisfied by the coördinates of the four points $(1,\,1)$, $(1, -1)$, $(-1,\,1)$, and $(-1, -1)$ only.

In what we have said it is understood that we mean points with coördinates which are real numbers. There are equations, such as $x^2 + y^2 = -1$, which are satisfied by no pair of real numbers x and y. Hence such equations have no graphical representation in our system of coördinates and are said to represent **imaginary loci.**

39. Summary. Experience will soon teach the student that no fixed rule for finding the graph of an equation will suffice. There are innumerable curves each with different properties, and methods which are effective in one case may not be effective in another. Proficiency in graphing can be attained only by drawing many curves and profiting by the experience gained. The student should, however, ask himself and answer the following questions whenever he has an equation whose graph is required:

(a) *Does the curve go through the origin?*

(b) *What are the intercepts on the axes?*

(c) *Is the curve symmetric with respect to one or both axes or the origin?*

(d) *Is the curve symmetric with respect to a line parallel to an axis?*

(e) *Can the equation be graphed by factoring?*

(f) *Are there any limitations on the values of the variables?*

(g) *Do any finite values of one variable make the other variable infinite?*

(h) *What are the equations of the asymptotes parallel to the axes if there are such asymptotes?*

(i) *Do both variables become infinite at the same time? If so, in which quadrant or quadrants?*

EXERCISES

Draw the graphs of the following equations after factoring their left members:

1. $x^2 - y^2 = 0$.

2. $x^2 - x - 6 = 0$.

3. $y^2 - 9 = 0$.

4. $x^2 y^2 - 2\,xy = 0$.

5. $2\,x^2 - 3\,xy - 2\,y^2 = 0$.

6. $x^4 - x^3 y - xy + y^2 = 0$.

Show that the following equations represent either isolated points or no real loci:

7. $x^2 + y^2 = 0$.

9. $(x - 1)^2 + (y + 2)^2 + 1 = 0$.

8. $x^2 + 4 = 0$.

10. $(x^2 - 1)^2 + (y - 1)^2 = 0$.

Sketch the graphs of the following equations:

11. $x^4 + x^2 y^2 = y^2$.

19. $y^2(x - 3)^2 = x$.

12. $x^2 y^2 = 4 - x^2$.

20. $y(x + 1)^2 = x$.

13. $y^2(1 + x) = 4$.

21. $y(x + 1)^2 = x^2$.

14. $y^2(x^2 + 1) = 4 x$.

22. $x - 2 y = 2 - xy$.

15. $y^2(6 - x) = x^3$.

23. $x^4 y^2 - x^2 y^4 = x^2 - y^2$.

16. $y^2(x - 1) = x$.

24. $x^2 + 2 xy + y^2 + 1 = 0$.

17. $y^2(x^2 - 1) = x$.

25. $y^2(x+2)^2(x-2)^2 = x(x^2-1)$.

18. $y^2(1 - x^2) = x$.

26. $xy^4 - 4 xy^2 - 4 = 0$.

40. Intersections of curves. If two curves are drawn on the same set of axes it is evident that the coördinates of the points of intersection of the two curves must satisfy the equation of each curve. Hence, to find the coördinates of the points of intersection of two curves, solve their equations simultaneously.

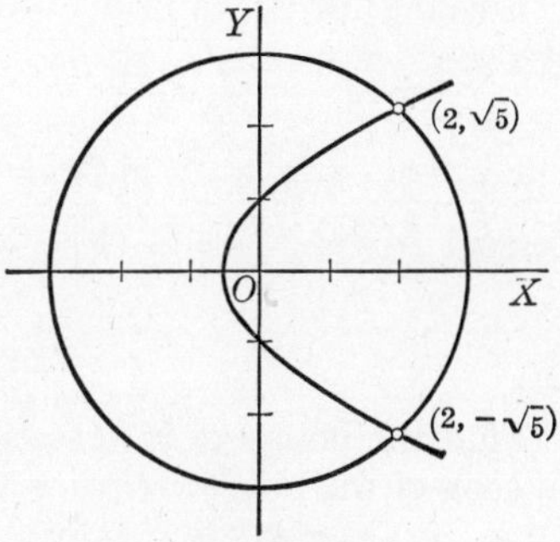

FIG. 32

EXAMPLE 1. Find the points of intersection of the curves

$$x^2 + y^2 = 9$$

and

$$y^2 = 2 x + 1.$$

Solving the two equations simultaneously, we have

$$x = 2, \ y = \pm \sqrt{5} \quad \text{and} \quad x = -4, \ y = \pm \sqrt{-7}.$$

Thus there are four pairs of algebraic solutions, only two of which are real. Hence the curves intersect in but two real points, $(2, \sqrt{5})$ and $(2, -\sqrt{5})$ (Fig. 32).

EXAMPLE 2. Find the points of intersection of $y^2 = x^3$ and $3x - y = 4$.

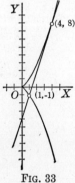

Eliminating y from the two equations, we have the equation

$$x^3 - 9x^2 + 24x - 16 = 0,$$

whose roots are found to be 1, 4, 4. Hence there are three pairs of solutions, $(1, -1)$ and $(4, 8)$ twice. The significance of the repeated solution $(4, 8)$ is shown in Fig. 33. At this point the line is tangent to the curve.

Two equations when treated simultaneously may have no solution or may have imaginary solutions only. In either case the graphs of the equations do not intersect.

FIG. 33

EXAMPLE 3. Find the points of intersection of $xy = 9$ and $x + y = 1$.

Solving for x, we find

$$x = \frac{1 \pm \sqrt{-35}}{2}.$$

Hence the two loci do not intersect in real points (Fig. 34).

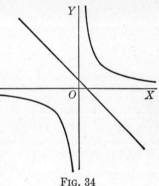

FIG. 34

EXERCISES

Find the points of intersection of the graphs of the equations in each of the following pairs and check graphically:

1. $3x - 2y = 6,$
   $y^2 - 6x = 0.$

2. $x^2 + y^2 = 10,$
   $x - 3y = 0.$

3. $8y - x^3 = 0,$
   $y - 2x = 0.$

4. $2y = x^2 + 1,$
   $3x - y = 4.$

5. $2x + y^2 = 6,$
   $x - y = 4.$

6. $x^2 + y^2 = 4,$
   $x^2 + y^2 = 9.$

7. $x^2 + y^2 = 20,$
   $xy - 8 = 0.$

8. $2y^2 - 9x = 0,$
   $3x^2 - 4y = 0.$

9. $2\,x^2 + y^2 = 72,$
   $y^2 - 7\,x^2 = 36.$

10. $y(x - 3) = 2\,x,$
    $2\,x - 3\,y = 0.$

11. $2(x + y) = xy,$
    $2\,x - y = 4.$

12. $x^2 + y^2 = 4,$
    $2\,x - y^2 = 6.$

13. $x^2 + y^2 = 9,$
    $y^2 - x = 3.$

14. $x^2 + y^2 = 4,$
    $y^2 - 2\,x = 5.$

15. $x - y = 2,$
    $y^2 - x^3 = 0.$

16. $7\,x - 3\,y = 4,$
    $y^2 - x^3 = 0.$

17. $x^2 + y = 10,$
    $x^2 - y^3 = 0.$

18. $3\,y - x^2 = 8,$
    $y^3 - 16\,x^2 = 0.$

19. $y(x^2 + 9) = 27,$
    $x + 2\,y = 6.$

20. $y(4 + x^2) = 2\,x^2,$
    $x - 2\,y = 0.$

21. $x^2 y - 1 = 0,$
    $y - 2\,x = 3.$

22. $x^2 y - 16 = 0,$
    $x^2 - 16\,y = 0.$

23. $x^2 - 2\,y = 0,$
    $x^3 - y = 0.$

24. $y^2 = x^3 + 1,$
    $y^2 = (x + 1)^3.$

25. $y^2 = x^3 + 1,$
    $2\,x - y = 1.$

26. $y = x(x - 2)^2,$
    $x - y = 0.$

27. $y^2 = x(x - 2)^2,$
    $x - y = 0.$

28. $4\,y = (4 - x^2)^2,$
    $4\,y - 8\,x = 1.$

29. Find the points of intersection of the curve $x^2 + y^2 = 20$ and the line $2\,x + y = c$. Determine c so that the line shall be tangent to the curve. (*Hint.* At the point of tangency the two points of intersection are coincident.)

30. Determine b so that the line $y = x + b$ shall be tangent to the curve $y^2 = 4\,x$.

31. Find m if the line $y = mx + b$ touches the curve $xy = 1$.

41. To find the equation of a given locus. The method of finding the equation corresponding to a given locus will vary from problem to problem. In general, the following steps should be taken in order:

(a) *Choose a suitable set of axes.* If the problem does not fix the axes, any suitable lines may be chosen. Generally some line of the figure suggested by the problem taken as an axis or some fixed point as origin will serve best. The best selection of axes is that which gives the simplest equation.

(b) *Locate all data with respect to these axes.*

(c) *Locate approximately on the graph a point satisfying the conditions of the problem and call its coördinates (x, y).*

(d) *Draw any auxiliary lines suggested by the conditions of the problem.*

(e) *Out of the figure thus constructed obtain an equation involving the coördinates (x, y) of the point whose locus is given.*

Relations of the sides of a right triangle, similar triangles, related slopes, and related distances are some of the possibilities for use in forming the desired equation.

Having found the equation, we may use it to aid in plotting the locus.

A locus is defined by giving some characteristic geometric property of it. From this property we derive an equation

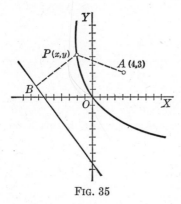

connecting the coördinates of any point on the locus. Then every other property of the locus is involved in the equation and may be obtained by an analysis of the equation.

FIG. 35

EXAMPLE 1. Find the equation of the locus of points which are equidistant from the line $4x + 3y + 25 = 0$ and from the point (4, 3).

Draw the line and locate the point on a set of axes. Select $P(x, y)$ any point on the locus and draw PA and PB. From the problem

$$PA = BP.$$

But $PA = \sqrt{(x-4)^2 + (y-3)^2}$ and $BP = \dfrac{4x + 3y + 25}{-5}$. Hence the required equation is

$$\frac{4x + 3y + 25}{-5} = \sqrt{(x-4)^2 + (y-3)^2}.$$

Squaring, clearing of fractions, and collecting terms, we have

$$9x^2 - 24xy + 16y^2 - 400x - 300y = 0.$$

EXAMPLE 2. Find the equation of the locus of a point which moves so that it is always three times as far from one end of a line segment as from the other, where the line segment is eight units long.

If we choose the midpoint of the line segment as origin and the line including the segment as the x-axis, the coördinates of the end points are $A(-4, 0)$ and $B(4, 0)$. By the condition of the problem $AP = 3\,BP$ or $BP = 3\,AP$. We shall solve the problem for $AP = 3\,BP$. Let (x, y) be the coördinates of P. Then $AP = \sqrt{(x+4)^2 + y^2}$ and $BP = \sqrt{(x-4)^2 + y^2}$.

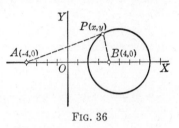

FIG. 36

Hence the equation of the locus of P is

$$\sqrt{(x+4)^2 + y^2} = 3\sqrt{(x-4)^2 + y^2}.$$

Squaring and reducing, we may write the equation in the form
$$x^2 + y^2 - 10\,x + 16 = 0.$$

The locus may be graphed from this equation.

A number of the succeeding chapters further illustrate the problem of finding the equation of a locus.

EXERCISES

1. What is the equation of the locus of points 3 units to the right of the y-axis? numerically 2 units from the x-axis?

2. Write the equation of the locus of points at a distance (a) 5 units from the origin; (b) 4 units from $(1, 2)$.

3. Write the equation of the locus of a point if the product of its distances from two fixed perpendicular lines is constant.

4. Find the equation of the locus of a point if the slope of the line joining it and the origin is twice its (a) abscissa; (b) ordinate.

5. Find the equation of the locus of a point whose distance from the origin is numerically equal to the slope of the line joining it and the origin.

6. A point moves so that the square of its distance from $(0, 3)$ diminished by the square of its distance from $(4, 0)$ is equal to the square of the distance between the given points. Find the equation of its locus.

7. Work Exercise 6 if the word "diminished" is replaced by the word "increased."

8. One of the equal sides of an isosceles triangle is fixed. Find the locus of the third vertex.

9. A point moves so that the sum of the squares of its distances from the ends of the hypotenuse of a right isosceles triangle is twice the square of its distance from the vertex of the right angle. Show that its path is along the hypotenuse (extended) of the triangle.

10. What is the equation of the locus of the centers of circles tangent to both axes?

11. Find the equation of the locus of points equidistant from the y-axis and $(3, 0)$.

12. Find the equation of the locus of points equidistant from the line $x = 3$ and $(-3, 0)$.

13. Find the equation of the locus of points equidistant from the line $y + 4 = 0$ and $(4, 0)$.

14. Find the equation of the locus of a point (a) whose distance from $(2, 0)$ is one half of its distance from the line $x - 8 = 0$; (b) whose distance from $(-2, 0)$ is one half of its distance from the line $x + 8 = 0$.

15. A point moves so that the sum of its distances from $(2, 0)$ and $(-2, 0)$ is 8. Find the equation of its locus.

16. Find the equation of the locus of a point whose distance from $(8, 0)$ is twice its distance from the line $x = 2$.

17. A point moves so that the difference of its distances from $(5, 0)$ and $(-5, 0)$ is 8. Find the equation of its locus.

18. Find the equation of the locus of points three times as far from $(8, 0)$ as from the origin.

19. Find the equation of the locus of points the sum of whose distances from $(1, 1)$ and $(-1, -1)$ is 4.

20. Find the equation of the locus of points equidistant from $(-\sqrt{2}, \sqrt{2})$ and the line $x - y = 2\sqrt{2}$.

21. A point moves so that the slope of the line joining it and $(-1, -3)$ is three times the slope of the line joining it and $(1, 1)$. Find the equation of its locus.

22. Given $A(-1, 0)$, $O(0, 0)$, and $B(1, 0)$. Find the locus of $P(x, y)$ if the product of the slopes of AP and BP equals the slope of OP.

23. A line segment of variable length has its ends on the coördinate axes and forms with them a triangle of constant area. Find the locus of its midpoint.

24. The triangle ABC has a fixed base $AB = 2 c$. Find the locus of the vertex C in each of the following cases:

    (a) The sum of the sides AC and BC is constant.
    (b) The difference of the sides AC and BC is constant.
    (c) The product of the sides AC and BC is constant.
    (d) The quotient of the sides AC and BC is constant.

42. Change of axes. It sometimes happens that the choice of axes made at the beginning of the solution of a problem does not give the simplest form of the equation. Two types of change of axes are in common use. They are called **translation** of axes and **rotation** of axes; they will be described and illustrated in the next two sections.

43. Translation. Translation of axes is a change from one set of axes to a new set parallel to the old axes. In Fig. 37 we shall express the coördinates (x, y) of the point P in terms of the coördinates (x', y') of the same point referred to the new axes $X'O'Y'$. The coördinates of O' are (h, k). From the figure we have

$$x = OM = ON + NM = h + x'$$

and

$$y = MP = MR + RP = k + y',$$

or $x = x' + h$ and $y = y' + k.$

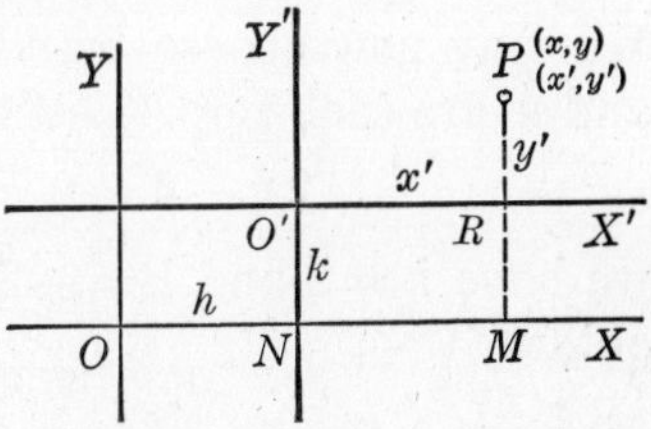

Fig. 37

The necessary substitutions for changing from the new axes back to the old are obtained by solving for x' and y'; they are

$$x' = x - h \quad \text{and} \quad y' = y - k.$$

EXAMPLE 1. In Example 2, Sec. 41, transform the equation $x^2 + y^2 - 10x + 16 = 0$ by translating the axes so that the origin is at $(5, 0)$.

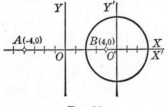

The equations of translation are

$$x = x' + 5 \quad \text{and} \quad y = y'.$$

FIG. 38

Substituting these values, we obtain

$$(x' + 5)^2 + y'^2 - 10(x' + 5) + 16 = 0,$$

or
$$x'^2 + y'^2 = 9,$$

thus changing the form of the equation but not changing the locus. By reference to the expression for the distance between two points, it is seen that the last equation states that the square of the distance from (x', y') to the origin is 9. Hence the point (x', y') lies on a circle of radius 3 with the center at the origin of the new axes, or with the center at the point $(5, 0)$ referred to the original axes.

EXAMPLE 2. Translate the axes to a new set of axes in such a way as to remove the x and y terms from the equation $x^2 + y^2 - 4x + 6y - 12 = 0$.

First method. Let $x = x' + h$ and $y = y' + k$ and collect terms. The result is

$$x'^2 + y'^2 + (2h - 4)x' + (2k + 6)y' + h^2 + k^2 - 4h + 6k - 12 = 0.$$

We may now choose h and k so that the coefficients of x' and y' are each zero. Letting

$$2h - 4 = 0 \quad \text{and} \quad 2k + 6 = 0,$$

we have $h = 2$ and $k = -3$. Substituting these values, we obtain
$$x'^2 + y'^2 - 25 = 0$$

as the equation of the locus referred to new axes, chosen so that there are no x' or y' terms in the equation. The new origin is at $(2, -3)$. The locus is a circle of radius 5 with the center at the new origin.

Second method. Upon completing squares in the equation $x^2 + y^2 - 4x + 6y - 12 = 0$, we may write

$$(x - 2)^2 + (y + 3)^2 - 25 = 0.$$

If we replace $x - 2$ by x' and $y + 3$ by y', we have

$$x'^2 + y'^2 - 25 = 0.$$

Hence the two methods of determining the translation lead to the same equation.

44. Rotation. Rotation of axes is changing from one set of axes to a new set which can be obtained by rotating the old axes about the origin. The problem is to express the coördinates (x, y) of a point P in terms of the coördinates (x', y') of the same point with respect to the axes $X'OY'$, which make the angle θ with the axes XOY. Drawing such auxiliary lines as are indicated in the figure, we see that

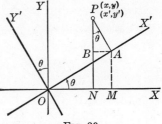

FIG. 39

$$x = ON = OM - NM = OM - BA$$
$$= OA \cos \theta - AP \sin \theta = x' \cos \theta - y' \sin \theta,$$

or $$x = x' \cos \theta - y' \sin \theta,$$

and $$y = NP = NB + BP = MA + BP$$
$$= OA \sin \theta + AP \cos \theta$$
$$= x' \sin \theta + y' \cos \theta,$$

or $$y = x' \sin \theta + y' \cos \theta.$$

The equations of rotation hold for any angle θ; that is, the transformed equation represents the same curve as the original equation no matter what value of θ is used. In many cases a value of θ can be chosen so that the transformed equation is simpler than the original equation. In Chapter V the student will learn how to choose a value of θ so as to remove the xy-term from a second-degree equation.

EXAMPLE. In Example 1, Sec. 41, transform the equation of the locus by rotating the axes through an angle θ such that $\sin \theta = \frac{3}{5}$ and $\cos \theta = \frac{4}{5}$.

The equations of rotation are

$$x = \tfrac{4}{5} x' - \tfrac{3}{5} y' \quad \text{and} \quad y = \tfrac{3}{5} x' + \tfrac{4}{5} y'.$$

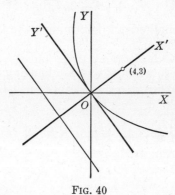

FIG. 40

Making these substitutions in the equation, we have

$$9\left(\frac{4\,x' - 3\,y'}{5}\right)^2 - 24\left(\frac{4\,x' - 3\,y'}{5}\right)\left(\frac{3\,x' + 4\,y'}{5}\right) + 16\left(\frac{3\,x' + 4\,y'}{5}\right)^2$$
$$- 400\left(\frac{4\,x' - 3\,y'}{5}\right) - 300\left(\frac{3\,x' + 4\,y'}{5}\right) = 0.$$

Reducing, we have $\quad y'^2 - 20\,x' = 0.$

EXERCISES

1. Simplify the equation $x^2 + y^2 - 6\,x - 8\,y - 11 = 0$ by translating the origin to $(3, 4)$.

2. Simplify the equation $x^2 + 2\,y^2 + 4\,x - 4\,y - 10 = 0$ by translating the origin to $(-2, 1)$.

3. Simplify the equation $y^2 - 8\,y - 2\,x + 18 = 0$ by translating the origin to $(1, 4)$.

4. Translate the axes so as to remove the first degree terms from the equation $x^2 + y^2 + 10\,x - 3\,y - 5 = 0$.

5. Translate the axes so as to remove the first degree terms from the equation $3\,x^2 - y^2 - 12\,x + 8\,y - 31 = 0$.

6. Remove the x-term from the equation $x^2 - 4x + 4y = 0$ by translating the axes. Can the y-term be removed by translating the axes?

7. The origin is translated to a point on the curve whose equation is $x^2 - 4x - 2y + 10 = 0$ so that the new y-axis is a line of symmetry. Write the transformed equation of the curve.

8. The origin is translated to the point of intersection of the lines $x + 2y - 5 = 0$ and $3x - 7y - 2 = 0$. Write the transformed equations of the lines.

9. The origin is translated to any point (h, k) on the line $Ax + By + C = 0$. Write the transformed equation of the line.

10. Draw the curve $y = (x - 2)^3$ after translating the origin to $(2, 0)$.

11. Draw the curve $(y - 1)^2 = (x + 3)^3$ after translating the origin to $(-3, 1)$.

12. Draw the curve $(y - 1)(x - 2) + 7 = 0$ after translating the origin to $(2, 1)$.

13. Translate the origin to a suitably chosen point and draw the curve of

(a) Exercise 1, page 50.   (c) Exercise 4, page 50.
(b) Exercise 3, page 50.   (d) Exercise 5, page 50.

14. Transform the equation $x^2 - y^2 = a^2$ by rotating the axes through $-45°$.

15. Transform the equation $2xy = a^2$ by rotating the axes through $45°$.

16. Simplify the equation derived in Exercise 19, page 58, by rotating the axes through $45°$.

17. Simplify the equation derived in Exercise 20, page 58, by rotating the axes through $-45°$.

18. Simplify the equation $41x^2 - 84xy + 104y^2 = 500$ by rotating the axes through the acute angle $\tan^{-1} \frac{1}{2}$.

19. Draw the curve $(x + y)^3 + 2(x - y) = 0$ after rotating the axes through $45°$.

20. Show that the equation $x^2 + y^2 = a^2$ is unchanged by a rotation of the axes.

45. Families of curves. EXAMPLE. Graph $y^2 = ax$.

If we assign a definite value to a, say $a = 1$, the equation $y^2 = x$ can be graphed as in Fig. 41. By assigning other values to a, $a = 2, 3, -1, -2$, etc., the corresponding curves

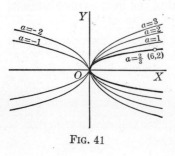

FIG. 41

can be graphed. The curves are all of the same general shape. Each depends upon the value given to the arbitrary constant, or parameter, a. Such a system of curves, derived from a single equation by giving different values to the parameter, is called a **family of curves**. If we want the curve of this family which passes through some given point, for example (6, 2), it is necessary to determine a so that the coördinates (6, 2) satisfy the equation. Substituting these coördinates in the equation $y^2 = ax$, we have

$$4 = 6\,a.$$

Hence a must equal $\frac{2}{3}$, and the desired equation is

$$y^2 = \tfrac{2}{3}\,x.$$

The graph is shown in Fig. 41 as the curve passing through (6, 2).

46. Functions and their graphs. If two variables are related in such a way that the value of one depends upon the value of the other, then the first is said to be a function of the second. Any algebraic expression in x is said to be a function of x. Thus, $x^2 + x$ is a function of x, and if we set $y = x^2 + x$, we say that x is the independent variable and the function, that is, y, is the dependent variable.

The graph may be used to illustrate the relation between the value of a function and the value of its independent variable. The graph may be used for this purpose even if it is impossible to write this relation by means of an equation. If we use ten-year periods beginning with 1790 as abscissas and the census returns as ordinates of points, a curve through these points will illustrate the population trend in this country. We shall be interested in this book, however, in those functions which have an analytic representation, that is, in those functions in which the relation between the function and the variable can be expressed in the form of an equation.

EXAMPLE 1. Graph the function $2x^2 - 3x + 1$.

In algebra we were chiefly interested in the zeros of such an expression. Let $y = 2x^2 - 3x + 1$ and graph. The curve (Fig. 42) not only shows the zeros of the function, but also

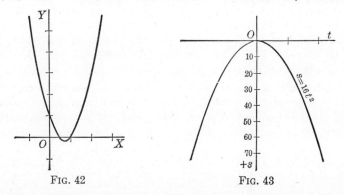

FIG. 42   FIG. 43

shows for what values of x the function is positive and for what values of x it is negative and gives some idea of the change in the function due to the change in x.

EXAMPLE 2. Show graphically the relation between the time t and the distance s a body would fall in a vacuum.

From physics we have $s = \frac{1}{2} gt^2$, s representing distance in feet and t representing time in seconds. Choosing the horizontal axis for the time axis and the vertical axis for the distance axis with positive s measured downward, we construct the graph as shown in Fig. 43, using $g = 32$. The part of the curve to the right of the s-axis represents the relation in which we are interested. The part of the curve to the left of the s-axis represents the relation that is shown by the equation but does not represent the physical problem.

MISCELLANEOUS EXERCISES

1. Discuss and draw the graphs of the following equations:

(a) $x^3 + y^3 = 8$;   (b) $x^4 + y^4 = 16$.

2. Find the intersections of the line $y = b$ with the curve $y = (x^2 - 1)^2$ and discuss the following cases: (a) $b < 0$; (b) $b = 0$; (c) $0 < b < 1$; (d) $b = 1$; (e) $b > 1$. Illustrate graphically.

3. Find the points of intersection of the graphs of the equations in each of the following pairs. Draw the figure in each case.

(a) $x + y = xy$,
$x^2 + y^2 = 8$.

(b) $x - 2y + 1 = 0$,
$y(x^2 + 3) = 4x$.

(c) $2x - y = 5$,
$y^2(10 - x) = x^3$.

(d) $x + y = 1$,
$y^2(5 - x) = 5 + x$.

(e) $3x - 4y + 15 = 0$,
$y^2(5 - x) = x^2(5 + x)$.

(f) $x - y = 1$,
$y^2 = (x - 1)^2(x - 2)$.

4. Show that the equations $x^2 - 2xy + y^2 - x + y - 12 = 0$ and $y^2 - y - 6 = 0$ represent lines which form a parallelogram, and find (a) the lengths of its sides; (b) the angle of intersection of its diagonals.

5. Show that $Ax^2 + Bxy + Cy^2 = 0$ represents (a) two distinct lines intersecting at the origin if $B^2 - 4AC > 0$, (b) two coincident lines if $B^2 - 4AC = 0$.

6. Discuss the locus which $Ax^2 + Bxy + Cy^2 = 0$ represents if $B^2 - 4AC < 0$.

7. What is the condition under which $Ax^2 + Bxy + Cy^2 = 0$ represents two perpendicular lines?

8. Draw several members of the family of curves $y = x^c$, using $c = 0, \pm 1, \pm 2, \pm 3, \pm \frac{1}{2}, \pm \frac{3}{2}, \pm \frac{2}{3}$, etc. What common property is possessed by every member of the family?

9. Draw several members of the family $y^2 = cx^3$. Select the member which passes through $(-2, 4)$.

10. Show that $f_1(x, y) + kf_2(x, y) = 0$ represents a family of curves passing through all the points of intersection of the two curves $f_1(x, y) = 0$ and $f_2(x, y) = 0$.

11. Write the equation of the family of curves passing through the points of intersection of the curves $y^2 = 8x$ and $y^2 = 12x - 8$. Find the equation of that member of the family which is a straight line.

12. Find the equation of the straight line through the points of intersection of the curves $x^2 + y^2 = 4$ and $x^2 + y^2 - 4x - 4y = 0$.

13. A point moves so that the slope of the line joining it and the origin equals n times the slope of the line joining it and $(a, 0)$. Discuss the position of its locus for $n = -3, -2, -1, 0, \frac{1}{2}, \frac{2}{3}, 1, 2, 3$.

14. The slope of a line through $(-a, 0)$ is n times the slope of a line through $(a, 0)$. Determine the nature of the locus of their point of intersection. Can n be chosen so that the locus will pass through $(a, 0)$? $(0, 0)$? $(-a, 0)$?

15. If the graph of $f(x)$ is a straight line, $f(x)$ is called a *linear function*. Show that $f(x) = mx + b$ is a linear function.

16. Graph $f(x) = 2x - 5$. For what values of x is $f(x)$ positive? zero? negative?

17. The equation $F = \frac{9}{5} C + 32$ expresses the relation between the Fahrenheit and centigrade thermometer readings. Draw an accurate graph of this equation and from the graph give the Fahrenheit readings corresponding to the following centigrade readings: $-5°, 0°, 20°, 32°$. Give the centigrade readings corresponding to the following Fahrenheit readings: $-12°, 0°, 15°, 32°$.

18. If a body is thrown upward with an initial velocity v_0, its velocity at any subsequent time t is given by the equation $v = v_0 - gt$, where g is approximately 32 when v is in feet and t in seconds. Graph this equation for $v_0 = 160$ feet per second. For what values of t is v positive? zero? negative?

19. A sum of money P at simple interest will in n years amount to $A = P + Prn$, where r is the interest rate. Graph this equation for (a) $P = \$100$ and $r = .06$; (b) $P = \$90$ and $r = .08$; (c) $P = \$75$ and $r = .08$. If (a) and (b) are graphed on the same axes explain the significance of the intersection of the graphs.

20. Graph $f(x) = 5 + 4x - x^2$. For what values of x is $f(x)$ positive? zero? negative? For what value of x does $f(x)$ have its largest positive value?

21. Illustrate graphically the values of x for which the function $f(x) = (x + 3)(x - 1)(x - 6)$ is positive; zero; negative.

22. Illustrate graphically that $f(x) = x^2 + x + 1$ is positive for all values of x.

23. Express the volume, total surface, and length of a diagonal of a cube as functions of one of its edges, and draw the graph of each of these functions.

24. Two masses, m_1 and m_2, at a distance of r units apart attract each other with a force F given by the equation $F = m_1 m_2 / r^2$. If $m_1 = 2$ and $m_2 = 5$, draw the graph showing the relation between F and r.

25. If a stone is thrown upward from the earth's surface with an initial velocity of 80 feet per second, the distance s, measured in feet, from the starting point in t seconds is given by the equation $s = 80\,t - \frac{1}{2}\,gt^2$. Assuming $g = 32$, illustrate graphically the relation between s and t.

26. According to Boyle's law the pressure and volume of a gas at a constant temperature are connected by the equation $PV = k$. Graph this equation for $k = 20$.

27. Equal squares of side x are cut from the corners of a piece of tin 12 inches square and the edges are folded up so as to form a box with an open top. Express the volume of the box as a function of x and draw the graph.

28. Estimate from the graph in Exercise 27 the value of x for which the volume of the box is largest.

29. One of the equal sides of an isosceles triangle is 6 inches. Express the area of the triangle as a function of the third side and draw the graph. Estimate from the graph the length of the third side for which the area is the largest.

CHAPTER IV

THE CIRCLE

47. Equation of a circle. A circle is the locus of points in a plane which are equidistant from a given point called the center.

Let (h, k) be the center of a circle of radius r. From the definition the distance from any point $P(x, y)$ on the circle to the center (h, k) is r. Hence the equation is

$$\sqrt{(x - h)^2 + (y - k)^2} = r,$$

or $\quad (x - h)^2 + (y - k)^2 = r^2. \quad (1)$

This may be written in the form

$$x^2 + y^2 + ax + by + c = 0, \quad (2)$$

where $a = -2h$, $b = -2k$, and $c = h^2 + k^2 - r^2$.

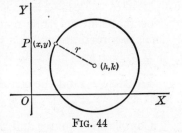

Fig. 44

Any circle is determined by its center and radius. Hence any circle can be represented by an equation like (2). For example, the circle whose radius is 5 and center $(-2, 3)$ is represented by the equation $x^2 + y^2 + 4x - 6y - 12 = 0$.

If the center of the circle is at the origin, $h = k = 0$, and equation (1) becomes

$$x^2 + y^2 = r^2.$$

48. Theorem. *The equation*

$$Ax^2 + Ay^2 + Bx + Cy + D = 0, \quad (A \neq 0) \quad (3)$$

in which the coefficients of x^2 and y^2 are equal and in which there is no xy term, represents a circle.

Dividing equation (3) by A, we have an equation of the form

$$x^2 + y^2 + ax + by + c = 0,$$

69

where $a = B/A$, $b = C/A$, and $c = D/A$. Completing the squares in the left member and transposing c, we have

$$x^2 + ax + \frac{a^2}{4} + y^2 + by + \frac{b^2}{4} = \frac{a^2}{4} + \frac{b^2}{4} - c,$$

or $$\left(x + \frac{a}{2}\right)^2 + \left(y + \frac{b}{2}\right)^2 = \frac{a^2}{4} + \frac{b^2}{4} - c. \tag{4}$$

Equation (4) is the condition that the distance from the point (x, y) to the fixed point $(-a/2, -b/2)$ is a constant. This condition is satisfied by any point (x, y) which lies on the circle whose center is $(-a/2, -b/2)$ and whose radius is $\sqrt{\frac{a^2}{4} + \frac{b^2}{4} - c}$, and by no other point. Hence equation (3) represents a circle.

If $a^2/4 + b^2/4 - c = 0$, equation (4) is satisfied by the coördinates of only one real point, $(-a/2, -b/2)$, and the locus is sometimes called a **point circle**.

If $a^2/4 + b^2/4 - c < 0$, there is no real locus.

EXAMPLE. Find the center and radius of the circle

$$x^2 + y^2 - 8x + 10y - 4 = 0.$$

Completing squares and rearranging, we may write

$$(x - 4)^2 + (y + 5)^2 = 45.$$

Comparing with equation (1), we see that the center of the circle is $(4, -5)$ and the radius is $r = \sqrt{45} = 3\sqrt{5}$. The circle should be drawn with the center and radius just found.

EXERCISES

1. Find the equations of the following circles and draw the circle in each case:

(a) With center at the origin and radius 4.

(b) With center at the origin and passing through $(6, 3)$.

(c) With center at $(6, 3)$ and passing through the origin.

(d) With ends of a diameter at $(-8, 10)$ and $(4, -2)$.

(e) With center at $(3, 5)$ and touching the x-axis.

(f) With center at $(3, 5)$ and touching the y-axis.

2. Write the equation of the circle of radius r tangent to both axes and lying in the (a) first quadrant; (b) second quadrant; (c) third quadrant; (d) fourth quadrant.

3. Find the equation of the circle which has for diameter that segment of the line $2x + 3y = 24$ included between the coördinate axes.

4. Find the equation of the circle with center at (9, 2) and touching the line $2x + y = 10$.

5. Reduce each of the following equations to the form of equation (1) (Sec. 47), determine the center and radius, and draw the circle. (As a partial check find the x- and y-intercepts of the circle.)

(a) $x^2 + y^2 - 4x - 8y + 4 = 0$.
(b) $x^2 + y^2 + 10x - 4y - 7 = 0$.
(c) $x^2 + y^2 - 8x + 7 = 0$.
(d) $x^2 + y^2 + 12y - 13 = 0$.
(e) $x^2 + y^2 = 6x + 6y$.
(f) $x^2 + y^2 - 4x - 2y + 5 = 0$.
(g) $2x^2 + 2y^2 - 3x + 5y = 3$.
(h) $3x^2 + 3y^2 + 4y - 7 = 0$.
(i) $5x^2 + 5y^2 - 20x + 12y = 33$.
(j) $x^2 + y^2 - 4x - 2y + 6 = 0$.
(k) $x^2 + y^2 - 2ax = 0$.
(l) $x^2 + y^2 - 2by = 0$.

6. Write the equation of the line of centers (the straight line containing the centers) of the circles $x^2 + y^2 - 6x + 5 = 0$ and $2x^2 + 2y^2 - 2x + 6y + 3 = 0$.

7. What form does equation (2) (Sec. 47) assume if the circle (a) passes through the origin? (b) has its center on the x-axis? (c) has its center on the y-axis? (d) has its center on the line $y = x$?

8. Write the equations of each of the following families of circles:

(a) With center at the origin.
(b) With center on the x-axis and passing through the origin.
(c) With center on the y-axis.
(d) With center on the line $y = x$ and passing through the origin.
(e) Touching the lines $y = \pm 6$.
(f) With center on the circle $x^2 + y^2 = 25$ and passing through the origin.

9. If two circles are concentric, how do their equations differ?

10. Write the equation of the circle passing through (4, 2) and concentric with the circle $x^2 + y^2 + 5x - 6y + 6 = 0$.

11. Show that the locus of points twice as far from (0, 3) as from (6, 0) is a circle and show its position relative to the given points.

12. Find the locus of a point such that the square of its distance from $(4, -3)$ is twice its distance from the y-axis.

49. Circle determined by three conditions. It will be observed that the general equation of the circle contains three independent constants. A circle can, therefore, be found that will satisfy three suitable conditions; for example, that will pass through three points not in a straight line. Suppose that (x_1, y_1), (x_2, y_2), and (x_3, y_3) are three points not in the same straight line. The equation of any circle may be written in the form

$$x^2 + y^2 + ax + by + c = 0.$$

If this circle passes through the three given points, the equation must be satisfied by the coördinates of each point. Substituting in turn the coördinates of the three points, we get the equations

$$x_1^2 + y_1^2 + ax_1 + by_1 + c = 0,$$
$$x_2^2 + y_2^2 + ax_2 + by_2 + c = 0,$$
$$x_3^2 + y_3^2 + ax_3 + by_3 + c = 0;$$

these will determine a, b, and c when solved simultaneously.

The equation of the circle may be used in the form

$$(x - h)^2 + (y - k)^2 = r^2,$$

in which case we have

$$(x_1 - h)^2 + (y_1 - k)^2 = r^2,$$
$$(x_2 - h)^2 + (y_2 - k)^2 = r^2,$$
$$(x_3 - h)^2 + (y_3 - k)^2 = r^2.$$

The simultaneous solution of these equations determines h, k, and r.

EXAMPLE 1. Find the equation of the circle through $(-2, -2)$, $(10, -8)$, and $(7, 1)$.

The three equations expressing the condition that the circle $x^2 + y^2 + ax + by + c = 0$ goes through the three points $(-2, -2)$, $(10, -8)$, and $(7, 1)$ are

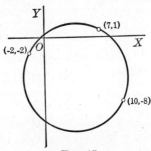

FIG. 45

$$4 + 4 - 2a - 2b + c = 0,$$
$$100 + 64 + 10a - 8b + c = 0,$$
$$49 + 1 + 7a + b + c = 0.$$

Solving simultaneously, we find $a = -8, b = 10,$ and $c = -4$. This gives the required equation,

$$x^2 + y^2 - 8x + 10y - 4 = 0.$$

EXAMPLE 2. Find the equation of the circle which is tangent to the line $3x - 4y - 20 = 0$, which has its center on the line $y = 2x$, and which passes through the point $(-2, -2)$.

The equation which expresses the condition that the center (h, k) of the circle is on the line $y = 2x$ is

$$k = 2h.$$

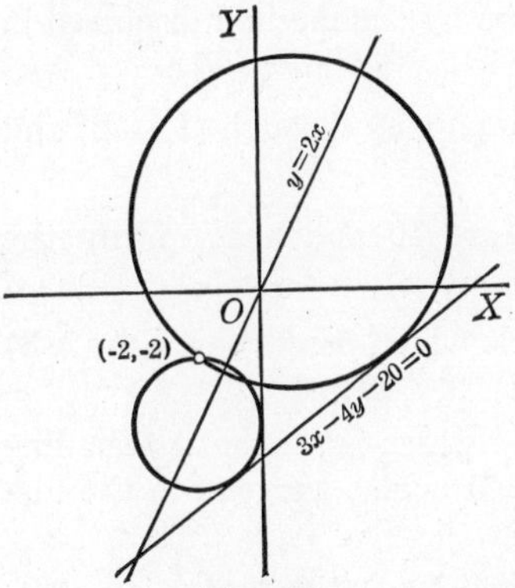

Since the circle is tangent to the line $3x - 4y - 20 = 0$, the distance from the line to the center is r. This condition is

$$\frac{3h - 4k - 20}{5} = -r,$$

in which $-r$ is used since the center is on the same side of the line as the origin. The condition that the circle passes through $(-2, -2)$ may be written

$$(-2 - h)^2 + (-2 - k)^2 = r^2.$$

FIG. 46

Solving the three equations simultaneously, we find two sets of values for $h, k,$ and r; namely, $h = 1, k = 2, r = 5$ and

$h = -2, k = -4, r = 2$. Hence there are two circles satisfying the conditions of the problem. The equations of the two circles are

$$(x - 1)^2 + (y - 2)^2 = 25$$

and

$$(x + 2)^2 + (y + 4)^2 = 4.$$

EXERCISES

1. Write the equation of the circle determined by the following points:

(a) (1, 1), (3, 2), and (2, − 1).
(b) (− 4, 1), (4, 5), and (4, − 7).
(c) (0, 5), (4, 3), and (2, − 1).
(d) (8, 11), (− 1, 14), and (11, − 10).

2. Write the equation of the circle circumscribing the triangle whose vertices are:

(a) (1, 3), (2, 1), and (7, − 1).
(b) (0, 0), (− 2, − 1), and (4, 5).
(c) (1, 3), (6, 2), and (11, − 5).
(d) (0, 0), (8, 4), and (1, 3).

3. Show that (1, 2), (4, 3), and (7, 4) are collinear. Try to find the equation of a circle through them by the method discussed in Sec. 49.

4. Find the equation of the circle passing through (1, − 2) and (5, − 4) if its center is on the line $x - y = 3$.

5. The x-intercepts of a circle are 10 and − 2. Write the equation of the circle if its center is on the line $2y = 3x$.

6. Write the equation of the circle which passes through (2, 8) and touches the y-axis at (0, 4).

7. Find the equation of the circle which is tangent to the line $x + 2y - 10 = 0$ at (10, 0) and which is also tangent to the line $x + 2y + 10 = 0$.

8. Write the equations of the two circles touching the line $x - y + 2 = 0$ with centers on the x-axis and with radii $4\sqrt{2}$.

9. Write the equation of the circle passing through (1, 6) and touching the line $x - 2y + 1 = 0$ at (− 1, 0).

10. Write the equations of the two circles with radii 10 and passing through (− 2, 3) and (6, − 1).

11. Find the equations of the two circles touching both axes and passing through $(4, 2)$.

12. Write the equations of the two circles each of which has its center on the line $4x - 2y = 5$ and is tangent to both axes.

13. Find the equations of the two circles touching the x-axis and passing through $(6, 2)$ and $(10, 10)$.

14. In each of the following cases find the equations of all the circles which are tangent to the line $3x + y = 3$ and pass through (a) $(3, 4)$ and $(1, 2)$; (b) $(3, 4)$ and $(5, -2)$; (c) $(3, 4)$ and $(-9, 6)$.

15. Write the equations of the two circles touching the lines $3x - 4y + 1 = 0$ and $4x + 3y - 7 = 0$ and passing through $(2, 3)$.

16. Find the equation of the circle inscribed in the triangle formed by the lines $x + y - 15 = 0$, $x - 7y - 11 = 0$, and $17x + 7y + 65 = 0$.

17. Find the equation of the circle tangent to the extensions of the first and third sides of the triangle in Exercise 16 and also tangent to the second side.

50. Circles through the intersections of two circles. The equation

$$(x^2 + y^2 + a_1x + b_1y + c_1) + k(x^2 + y^2 + a_2x + b_2y + c_2) = 0 \quad (5)$$

represents a circle through the points of intersection of the circles

$$x^2 + y^2 + a_1x + b_1y + c_1 = 0 \quad \text{and} \quad x^2 + y^2 + a_2x + b_2y + c_2 = 0$$

for every value of k except for $k = -1$. Equation (5) represents a circle because it can be put in the form of equation (3) (Sec. 48). It will pass through the points of intersection of the two circles for every k, since the coördinates of the points of intersection make each expression in parenthesis equal to zero. Equation (5) contains the parameter k. By the proper choice of k we can make the circle (5) satisfy one more suitable condition. It should be kept in mind that equation (5) already satisfies two conditions, since the circle represented by (5) passes through the two points of intersection of two circles.

In case $k = -1$, equation (5) reduces to

$$(a_1 - a_2)x + (b_1 - b_2)y + c_1 - c_2 = 0.$$

This is the equation of the line through the points of intersection of the two circles. The common chord is a segment of this line. If the circles do not intersect, the line does not

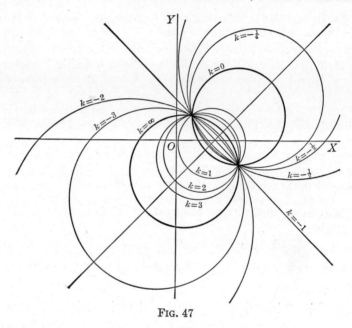

FIG. 47

intersect either circle. In either case the line is called the **radical axis**.

Members of the family of curves

$$x^2 + y^2 - 16\,x - 6\,y + 37 + k(x^2 + y^2 - 2\,x + 8\,y - 33) = 0$$

through the points of intersection of the circles

$$x^2 + y^2 - 16\,x - 6\,y + 37 = 0$$

and $$x^2 + y^2 - 2\,x + 8\,y - 33 = 0$$

are drawn in the accompanying figure for $k = -3, -2, -1,$ $-\frac{1}{2}, -\frac{1}{3}, -\frac{1}{4}, 1, 2,$ and 3.

51. Distance from a point to a circle along a tangent. From a point $P(x', y')$ outside the circle (Fig. 48)

$$(x - h)^2 + (y - k)^2 - r^2 = 0 \qquad (6)$$

draw the tangent PT and the line PC. The triangle CTP has a right angle at T. Hence

$$\overline{PT}^2 = \overline{PC}^2 - \overline{CT}^2$$
$$= (x' - h)^2 + (y' - k)^2 - r^2.$$

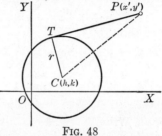

FIG. 48

We observe that the expression for $\overline{PT}^2$ can be obtained by substituting x' and y' for x and y, respectively, in the left member of equation (6). Therefore, if the coördinates of a point outside the circle are substituted in the left member of the equation of the circle in the form (6), that expression is no longer zero, but is the square of the distance from the point to the circle measured along the tangent. The equation

$$x^2 + y^2 + ax + by + c = 0,$$

being a rearrangement of

$$(x - h)^2 + (y - k)^2 - r^2 = 0,$$

may be used instead of the latter form to find this distance.

Assume that (x', y') is a point from which the distances to the two circles

$$x^2 + y^2 + a_1x + b_1y + c_1 = 0,$$
$$x^2 + y^2 + a_2x + b_2y + c_2 = 0$$

measured along the tangents are equal. Then

$$x'^2 + y'^2 + a_1x' + b_1y' + c_1 = x'^2 + y'^2 + a_2x' + b_2y' + c_2,$$

or $\qquad (a_1 - a_2)x' + (b_1 - b_2)y' + c_1 - c_2 = 0.$

But this is the condition that the point (x', y') lies on the radical axis. Hence *the radical axis of two circles is the locus of all points from which tangents of equal length may be drawn to the two circles.*

EXERCISES

Write the equation of the circle through the points of intersection of the following circles:

1. $x^2 + y^2 + 2x - 6y = 15$ and $x^2 + y^2 - 12x - 10y + 45 = 0$ and through the origin.

2. $x^2 + y^2 + 4x - 4y = 17$ and $x^2 + y^2 - 8x + 2y + 7 = 0$ and through $(4, 3)$.

3. $x^2 + y^2 - 8x - 4y = 16$ and $x^2 + y^2 + 2x + 6y - 16 = 0$ and through the center of the first circle.

4. $x^2 + y^2 - x - 5y + 1 = 0$ and $x^2 + y^2 + 7x - y - 3 = 0$ and with its center on (*a*) the x-axis; (*b*) the line $x - y = 0$.

5. Write the equations of the radical axes of the given pairs of circles in Exercises 1, 2, 3, and 4.

6. Find the distance from $(5, 10)$ measured along the tangent line to the circle $x^2 + y^2 - 6x + 2y - 15 = 0$.

7. Find the distance measured along the tangent line to each of the circles $x^2 + y^2 = 20$ and $x^2 + y^2 - 18x - 6y + 40 = 0$ from each of the following points: (*a*) $(0, 10)$; (*b*) $(2, 4)$; (*c*) $(3, 1)$; (*d*) $(4, -2)$; (*e*) $(6, -8)$. Draw the figure.

8. Find the equation of the radical axis of the two circles in Exercise 7.

9. Show in two different ways that the point $(3, 7)$ is on the radical axis of the two circles $x^2 + y^2 - 3x + 5y - 34 = 0$ and $x^2 + y^2 - 19x - 3y + 70 = 0$.

10. A circle of radius 4 has its center at the origin. The center of a circle of radius 2 moves along the x-axis. Discuss the position of the radical axis of the two circles when the center of the second circle is at (*a*) $(8, 0)$; (*b*) $(6, 0)$; (*c*) $(4, 0)$; (*d*) $(2, 0)$; (*e*) $(0, 0)$.

11. Determine the length of the common chord of the two circles $x^2 + y^2 - 12x + 2y - 13 = 0$ and $x^2 + y^2 - 16x + 5y - 11 = 0$.

12. Show that the circle $x^2 + y^2 + 6x + 12y - 45 = 0$

(*a*) intersects the circle $x^2 + y^2 - 22x - 2y - 3 = 0$ in two distinct points;

(*b*) is tangent to the circle $x^2 + y^2 - 18x + 4y + 75 = 0$;

(*c*) does not intersect the circle $x^2 + y^2 - 14x - 8y + 55 = 0$.

13. Show that the radical axes of any three circles, the circles being taken in pairs, intersect in a common point (radical center) or are parallel.

14. Find the radical center of the circles $x^2 + y^2 + 6x - 8y = 0$, $x^2 + y^2 - 14x + 40 = 0$, and $x^2 + y^2 - 6x + 16y + 72 = 0$.

MISCELLANEOUS EXERCISES

1. Write the equations of the two circles with centers at the origin which touch the circle $x^2 + y^2 - 4x - 2y - 40 = 0$.

2. Write the equation of the circle concentric with the circle $x^2 + y^2 - 2x - 4y = 0$ and tangent to the line $x + 2y - 15 = 0$.

3. Find the equation of the circle circumscribing the equilateral triangle whose vertices are $(-a, 0)$, $(a, 0)$, and $(0, a\sqrt{3})$.

4. Find the midpoint of the chord which is cut from the line $x + 3y - 11 = 0$ by the circle $x^2 + y^2 - x + 3y - 30 = 0$.

5. Find the points on the line $x + 2y - 9 = 0$ each at a distance of 5 units from $(2, 1)$.

6. A line segment $2\sqrt{5}$ units in length lies along the line $x - 2y + 4 = 0$. Find the coördinates of its end points if its midpoint is $(4, 4)$.

7. Write the equations of the two circles touching the line $3x + y - 6 = 0$ at $(1, 3)$ and having radii $2\sqrt{10}$.

8. Write the equation of the line tangent to the circle $x^2 + y^2 - 4x + 4y - 9 = 0$ at $(1, 2)$.

9. Write the equations of the two lines with slope 3 which are tangent to the circle $x^2 + y^2 = 40$.

10. Show that the line $2x - 3y + 8 = 0$ is tangent to the circle $x^2 + y^2 - 2x + 2y - 11 = 0$ and find

(a) the equation of the tangent parallel to it.
(b) the equations of the two tangents perpendicular to it.

11. Tangents are drawn from the point $(6, -10)$ to the circle $x^2 + y^2 - 12x - 20y - 64 = 0$. Find the points where they touch the circle.

12. Write the equations of the four circles each of radius 1 unit which are tangent to the x-axis and to the line $y = mx$.

13. Show that the equation of the line tangent to the circle $x^2 + y^2 = r^2$ at the point (x_1, y_1) on the circle is $x_1 x + y_1 y = r^2$.

14. Show that the equations of the two tangents to the circle $x^2 + y^2 = r^2$ with slope m are $y = mx \pm r\sqrt{1 + m^2}$.

15. Show that the quadrilateral whose vertices are $(10, 10)$, $(1, 13)$, $(-14, -2)$, and $(13, -11)$ can be circumscribed by a circle.

16. In Exercise 15 select any one of the four points. Drop perpendiculars from it upon the sides of the triangle whose vertices are the other three points. Show that the feet of these perpendiculars are collinear.

17. The vertices of a triangle are $A(5, 10)$, $B(7, 4)$, and $C(-9, -4)$. The medians AD, BE, and CF intersect at G. The altitudes AK, BL, and CM intersect at H. The midpoints of AH, BH, and CH are R, S, and T, respectively. Show that the nine points D, E, F, K, L, M, R, S, and T lie on a circle whose center is on the line joining G and H and divides GH in the ratio $1:3$.

18. Prove analytically that an angle inscribed in a semicircle is a right angle.

19. Prove analytically that all angles inscribed in the same segment of a circle are equal.

20. Show that the perpendicular dropped from any point of a circle upon a diameter is a mean proportional between the segments into which it divides the diameter.

21. A point moves so that the square of its distance from a given point equals its distance from a given line. Show that its locus is a circle.

22. Find the locus of a point if its distances from two fixed points are in a constant ratio k $(k \neq 1)$.

23. Show that the locus of a point, the sum of the squares of whose distances from n fixed points is constant, is a circle.

24. A point moves so that the sum of the squares of its distances from two vertices of an equilateral triangle equals the square of its distance from the third vertex. Show that the locus is a circle and determine its position relative to the triangle.

25. Find the equation of the locus of a point if lines drawn from it to two fixed points include an angle of $45°$.

26. A rod 10 inches long has its ends moving on two perpendicular lines. Find the locus of its midpoint.

CHAPTER V

OTHER SECOND DEGREE CURVES

THE PARABOLA

52. Definition and equation of a parabola. *A parabola is the locus of points which are equidistant from a fixed point and a fixed straight line.* The fixed point is called the **focus** and the fixed line is called the **directrix** of the parabola.

In Fig. 49 (*a* and *b*) let *AB* be the directrix, and let *F* be the focus. Draw a line through *F* perpendicular to *AB* and

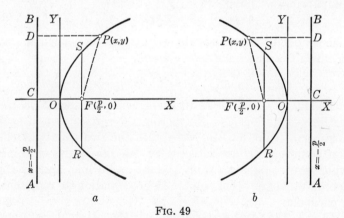

FIG. 49

intersecting it in *C*. By definition, the midpoint *O* of *CF* is a point on the parabola. Choosing *O* as origin and the line through *C* and *F* as the *x*-axis, we denote the coördinates of *F* by $(p/2, 0)$, where p is the distance from the directrix to the focus and is a positive number in Fig. 49 *a* and a negative number in Fig. 49 *b*. The equation of the directrix in each

81

case is $x = - p/2$. Let $P(x, y)$ be any point on the parabola and draw FP and DP. By definition,

$$FP = DP \text{ in Fig. 49 } a$$

and $\qquad\qquad FP = PD = - DP$ in Fig. 49 b.

But $\quad FP = \sqrt{\left(x - \frac{p}{2}\right)^2 + y^2}$, and $DP = x + \frac{p}{2}$;

hence $\qquad \sqrt{\left(x - \frac{p}{2}\right)^2 + y^2} = x + \frac{p}{2}$ in Fig. 49 a

and $\qquad \sqrt{\left(x - \frac{p}{2}\right)^2 + y^2} = -\left(x + \frac{p}{2}\right)$ in Fig. 49 b. $\left.\begin{array}{c} \\ \\ \\ \end{array}\right\}$ (1)

Either form of equation (1) reduces to

$$x^2 - px + \frac{p^2}{4} + y^2 = x^2 + px + \frac{p^2}{4}. \qquad (2)$$

Simplifying, we have

$$y^2 = 2\,px. \qquad (3)$$

The simplicity of this equation is due to the particular way in which the axes have been chosen.

Conversely, the equation $y^2 = 2\,px$ represents a parabola.

Adding $x^2 - px + p^2/4$ to each member of equation (3), we have equation (2). Extracting the square root of each member of equation (2), we obtain the two equations (1). But equations (1) are satisfied by the coördinates of points which are equidistant from a point and a line, and by the coördinates of no other points. Hence equation (3) represents a parabola.

In case the focus of a parabola is the point $(0,\ p/2)$ and the directrix is the line $y = - p/2$, the equation of the parabola is $\qquad\qquad x^2 = 2\,py,\qquad\qquad (4)$

where p is positive if the focus is above the directrix and is negative if the focus is below the directrix.

It will be observed that p is the distance from directrix to focus.

53. Discussion of the equation. Solving equation (3) for y, we have
$$y = \pm \sqrt{2\,px}.$$

If p is positive (as shown in Fig. 49 a), x must be positive in order that y may be real. Hence the curve lies to the right of the y-axis. If p is negative, x must be negative, and the curve lies to the left of the y-axis (Fig. 49 b). To each value of x correspond two values of y, numerically equal but opposite in sign; hence the curve is symmetric with respect to the x-axis. As x increases numerically, y increases numerically and the curve extends indefinitely away from both axes. The line of symmetry is called the **axis** of the parabola, and the point of intersection of the parabola and its axis is called the **vertex** of the parabola. The double ordinate RS through the focus is called the **latus rectum.**

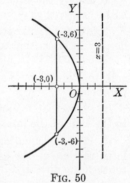

FIG. 50

EXAMPLE. Discuss and graph the parabola $y^2 = -12\,x$.

There is symmetry with respect to the x-axis. The parabola passes through the origin and does not cut either axis elsewhere. The curve lies to the left of the y-axis since x must be negative to give real values for y. The vertex of the parabola is at the origin. The distance from the directrix to the focus is $p = -6$; hence the focus is at $(-3, 0)$ and the equation of the directrix is $x = 3$. The length of the latus rectum is 12. The graph is shown in the figure.

EXERCISES

1. Find the coördinates of the focus, the length of the latus rectum, and the equation of the directrix of each of the following parabolas and sketch:

(a) $y^2 = 4\,x$.   (c) $x^2 = 12\,y$.   (e) $2\,y^2 = 5\,x$.

(b) $y^2 = -6\,x$.   (d) $x^2 = -3\,y$.   (f) $5\,x^2 = 2\,y$.

2. Find the equations of the two parabolas through each of the following points, one with axis along the x-axis and the other with axis along the y-axis, the vertex of each parabola being at the origin: (a) $(3, 1)$; (b) $(5, -3)$; (c) $(-10, 4)$; (d) $(-\frac{1}{2}, -\frac{2}{3})$; (e) $(6, 6)$.

3. Find the length of the latus rectum of the parabola $y^2 = 2\,px$.

4. Draw on the same set of axes the parabolas $y^2 = 2\,px$ for $p = \frac{1}{2}, 1, 2, 3, 4$. What effect does the changing of the value of p have upon the shape of the parabola?

5. Using the definition, write the equations of the following parabolas:

    (a) Focus at $(0, 0)$, directrix $x = 4$.
    (b) Focus at $(0, 0)$, directrix $x = -4$.
    (c) Focus at $(1, -3)$, directrix $y = 1$.
    (d) Focus at $(1, -\frac{3}{4})$, directrix $y = -\frac{5}{4}$.

6. Derive the equation of a parabola with focus at $(p, 0)$ and with the y-axis as directrix.

7. By a suitable translation of axes transform the equation derived in Exercise 6 to the form of (3), Sec. 52.

8. Show that the locus of the center of the circle which is tangent to a given line and which passes through a fixed point is a parabola.

9. Show that for any parabola the two lines from the vertex to the ends of the latus rectum include a constant angle.

10. Find the equation of the circle which has for a diameter the latus rectum of the parabola $y^2 = 2\,px$. Show that the circle touches the directrix.

11. Find the equation of the circle through the vertex and the ends of the latus rectum of the parabola $y^2 = 8\,x$.

12. An isosceles right triangle is inscribed in the parabola $y^2 = 2\,px$ so that the vertex of the right angle is at the origin. Find the length of the hypotenuse.

13. The vertex of a parabola with axis on the x-axis is at the origin. Find the length of that chord through the focus which has one end at $(1, 4)$.

14. An arch in the form of an arc of a parabola with its vertex at the center of the arch is 18 feet across at the base and its highest point is 8 feet above the base. What is the length of a beam parallel to the base and 6 feet above it?

15. The cable of a suspension bridge hangs in the shape of an arc of a parabola. The supporting towers are 70 feet high and 200 feet apart and the lowest point on the cable is 20 feet above the roadway. Find the length of a supporting rod 50 feet from the middle of the bridge.

16. Show that the abscissas of any two points on the parabola $y^2 = 2\,px$ have the same ratio as the squares of their ordinates.

54. Vertex not at the origin. It is frequently necessary or convenient to study the parabola when the vertex is not at the origin. We shall obtain the equation when the vertex of the parabola is at $(h,\ k)$ and the axis of the curve is a line parallel to the x-axis.

Draw through the point $(h,\ k)$ lines parallel to the x- and y-axes. If these lines are used as x'- and y'-axes, the vertex of the parabola will be at the origin and its equation will be

$$y'^2 = 2\,px'.$$

But $x = x' + h$ and $y = y' + k$, or $x' = x - h$ and $y' = y - k$.

Making these substitutions, we obtain

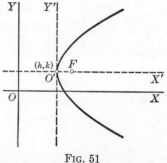

Fig. 51

$$(y - k)^2 = 2\,p(x - h). \quad (5)$$

This is, therefore, the equation of a parabola with vertex at $(h,\ k)$ and with axis parallel to the x-axis. Similarly, for a parabola with vertex at $(h,\ k)$ and with axis parallel to the y-axis, the equation is

$$(x - h)^2 = 2\,p(y - k). \tag{6}$$

It will be noted that equations (5) and (6) become equations (3) and (4), respectively, for $h = k = 0$.

The translation of axes leaves unchanged the position of the focus and directrix with respect to the parabola.

Any equation of the form (5) or (6) can be put in the form of (3) or (4), respectively, by a translation of axes, and hence such an equation represents a parabola.

55. Theorem. *In general,* the equations*

$$Ay^2 + Bx + Cy + D = 0 \tag{7}$$

and $\qquad A'x^2 + B'x + C'y + D' = 0 \tag{8}$

represent parabolas.

By completing squares and rearranging terms, the equations (7) and (8) can be put in the form of (5) and (6), respectively, and hence represent parabolas.

EXAMPLE. Discuss and graph $y^2 - 6x - 8y - 2 = 0$. Transposing and completing the square, we may write

$$y^2 - 8y + 16 = 6x + 18,$$

or $\qquad (y - 4)^2 = 6(x + 3).$

The parabola represented by this equation has its vertex at $(-3, 4)$ and has for axis the line $y = 4$. The distance from

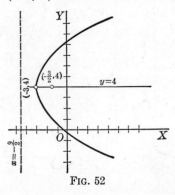

FIG. 52

directrix to focus is given by $2p = 6$, or $p = 3$. Since p is positive, the parabola opens toward the right. The focus is $\frac{3}{2}$ units to the right of the vertex and hence is $(-\frac{3}{2}, 4)$. The directrix is $x = -\frac{9}{2}$. The graph is shown in Fig. 52.

56. Scientific applications of the parabola. In the following illustrations either an arc of a parabola is used or the variable quantities are related in the same manner as the coördinates of a point on a parabola. The list is meant to be suggestive of the many applications of the parabola.

(*a*) The cable of a suspension bridge hangs in the form of an arc of a parabola.

(*b*) Some of the largest steel bridges are built with arches which are arcs of parabolas.

---

* Exceptions occur if the constants are such that the equations reduce to the first degree, or if the left members factor into first degree factors (see Sec. 37).

(c) A reflecting surface made by rotating a parabola about its axis will send the light out in parallel rays if the source of light is at the focus.

(d) The large reflector in a reflecting telescope is usually parabolic.

(e) The path of a projectile, if air resistance is neglected, is a parabola.

(f) The equation expressing the relation between the distance a freely falling body traverses and the time required is the equation of a parabola.

(g) The equation expressing the relation between the period and the length of a simple pendulum is the equation of a parabola.

(h) The equation expressing the relation between the bending moment at a point on a uniformly loaded beam and the distance from the point of support is the equation of a parabola.

(i) If a cylindrical vessel partly filled with water is whirled about the axis of the cylinder, a plane through the axis will cut the surface of the water in a parabola.

EXERCISES

1. Determine the vertex, focus, length of latus rectum, directrix, and axis of each of the following parabolas and sketch:

(a) $y^2 - 2y - 8x + 25 = 0$.   (d) $2x^2 - 10x + 5y = 0$.

(b) $y^2 + 6y + 6x = 0$.   (e) $3y^2 = 8x - 16$.

(c) $x^2 - 4x - 2y - 8 = 0$.   (f) $5x^2 + 4y = 12$.

2. Write the equations of the following parabolas and sketch:

(a) Directrix $x + 2 = 0$, vertex at $(1, 3)$.

(b) Directrix $y = 3$, vertex at $(-2, 2)$.

(c) Directrix $y = 0$, focus at $(3, 1)$.

(d) Directrix $x = 5$, focus at $(-1, 0)$.

(e) Vertex at $(-\frac{5}{2}, 1)$, focus at $(0, 1)$.

3. Write the equations of the two lines through the vertex and the ends of the latus rectum of the parabola $y^2 - 4y - 6x - 2 = 0$.

4. Find the length of the common chord of the parabolas $y^2 = 2x + 12$ and $y^2 + 2y = 4x$. Draw the figure.

5. Find the equation of the parabola with vertex at $(2, 1)$ and passing through $(5, -2)$ with axis (a) parallel to the x-axis; (b) parallel to the y-axis.

6. Given the equation $y = ax^2 + bx + c$,

(a) show that it represents a parabola with axis parallel to the y-axis;

(b) show that the parabola is concave upward if $a > 0$; downward if $a < 0$;

(c) find the x-intercepts. Under what condition are they real and distinct? real and equal? imaginary?

(d) show that the axis of the parabola is the line $x = -b/2\,a$;

(e) show that the vertex of the parabola is $\left(-\dfrac{b}{2\,a}, \dfrac{4\,ac - b^2}{4\,a}\right)$;

(f) discuss the position of the parabola if $c = 0$; $b = 0$; $b = c = 0$.

7. Find the x- and y-intercepts, the axis, and the vertex of each of the following parabolas and sketch:

(a) $y = x^2 - 6\,x + 5$. (e) $2\,y = 2\,x^2 - 3\,x - 2$.

(b) $y = 3 + 2\,x - x^2$. (f) $y = x^2 - 4\,x$.

(c) $y = 4\,x^2 - 12\,x + 9$. (g) $y = -(x + 3)^2$.

(d) $y = 2\,x^2 - 2\,x + 1$. (h) $3\,y = -(6 + x^2)$.

8. Find the equation of the parabola through $(1, -2)$, $(2, 1)$, and $(-1, 4)$ with axis parallel to the (a) y-axis; (b) x-axis.

9. A parabola with axis parallel to the x-axis passes through $(3, 3)$, $(6, -3)$, and $(11, 7)$. Find its focus and directrix without finding its equation.

THE ELLIPSE

57. Definition and equation of an ellipse. *An ellipse is the locus of points the sum of whose distances from two fixed points is constant.* The two fixed points are the **foci** of the ellipse.

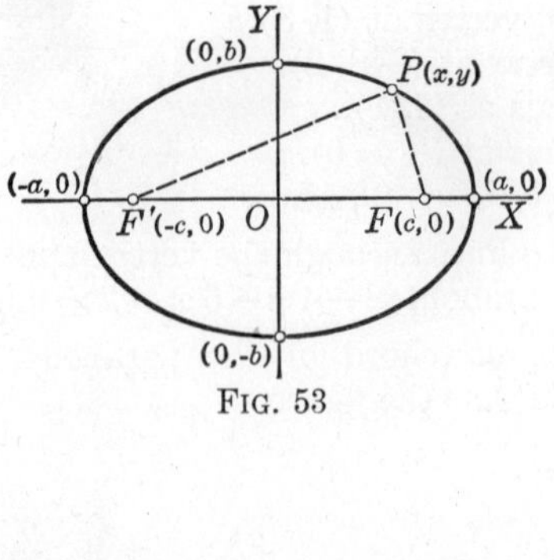

Fig. 53

Let the distance between the fixed points be $2\,c$, and let the constant sum be $2\,a$, $(a > c)$. If we choose the line through the foci as the x-axis and the point midway between the foci as origin, the coördinates of the foci are $(c, 0)$ and $(-c, 0)$. By definition

$$F'P + FP = 2a,$$

or $\qquad \sqrt{(x+c)^2 + y^2} + \sqrt{(x-c)^2 + y^2} = 2a.$

Transposing the second radical, squaring, and reducing, we have

$$cx - a^2 = -a\sqrt{(x-c)^2 + y^2}.$$

Squaring again and reducing, we may write

$$x^2(a^2 - c^2) + a^2 y^2 = a^2(a^2 - c^2).$$

Since $a > c$, let $b^2 = a^2 - c^2$. Making this substitution and dividing by $a^2 b^2$, we obtain

$$\frac{x^2}{a^2} + \frac{y^2}{b^2} = 1. \qquad (9)$$

If the foci are the points $(0, c)$ and $(0, -c)$, the equation of the ellipse is

$$\frac{x^2}{b^2} + \frac{y^2}{a^2} = 1. \qquad (10)$$

Conversely, any equation of the form (9) *or* (10) *represents an ellipse.* The proof will not be set down here. It consists in showing that the steps used in obtaining equations (9) and (10) can be reversed, as was done in the case of the parabola.

58. Discussion of the equation. Equation (9) shows that the locus is symmetric with respect to both axes and hence is symmetric with respect to the origin. Solving for y, we have

$$y = \pm \frac{b}{a}\sqrt{a^2 - x^2};$$

whence it appears that real values of y exist only when $x^2 \leqq a^2$. Hence the curve lies between the lines $x = a$ and $x = -a$. The largest numerical value is attained by y when $x = 0$; hence the curve lies between the lines $y = b$ and $y = -b$. The x-intercepts are $\pm a$ and the y-intercepts are $\pm b$. The segment of the line of symmetry through the foci, from $(-a, 0)$ to $(a, 0)$, of length $2a$, is called the **major axis** of the ellipse. The segment of the line of symmetry at right angles to the major axis, from $(0, -b)$ to $(0, b)$, of length $2b$, is called the **minor axis**. The lengths a and b are the semimajor and semiminor axes, respectively. The point of intersection of the major and minor axes is the **center** since the ellipse is symmetric with respect to this point. The ends of the major axis are the **vertices** of the ellipse.

A similar discussion of equation (10) will show that it represents the same curve with major axis along the y-axis.

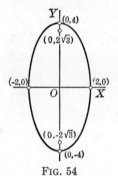

Fig. 54

EXAMPLE. Graph the ellipse $4x^2+y^2=16$ and find its semiaxes and foci.

The equation shows symmetry with respect to both axes. Dividing by 16, we obtain

$$\frac{x^2}{4} + \frac{y^2}{16} = 1.$$

The equation shows that the major axis lies along the y-axis. The semimajor axis is $a = 4$ and the semiminor axis is $b = 2$. The vertices of the ellipse are at $(0, \pm 4)$ and the ends of the minor axis are at $(\pm 2, 0)$. From $b^2 = a^2 - c^2$, we have $c = 2\sqrt{3}$. Hence the foci are at $(0, \pm 2\sqrt{3})$. The ellipse is shown in the figure.

59. Eccentricity. Location of foci. The ratio c/a, denoted by e, is called the **eccentricity** of the ellipse. Since $c^2 = a^2 - b^2$, we may write

$$e = \frac{\sqrt{a^2 - b^2}}{a}.$$

This shows that as b approaches a, the eccentricity e approaches zero. But for $b = a$, the locus is a circle. Hence the circle is sometimes called an ellipse of eccentricity zero.

From the equation connecting a, b, and c, it is seen that a is the hypotenuse of a right triangle with legs b and c. Hence the distance from the end of the minor axis to a focus is a. The foci may, therefore, be located by drawing an arc with an end of the minor axis as center and a radius equal to a. The points in which the arc cuts the major axis are the foci.

EXERCISES

1. Find the semiaxes, eccentricity, and foci of the following ellipses and sketch:

(a) $\dfrac{x^2}{36} + \dfrac{y^2}{16} = 1.$

(b) $\dfrac{x^2}{9} + \dfrac{y^2}{25} = 1.$

(c) $x^2 + 3\,y^2 = 12.$

(d) $9\,x^2 + y^2 = 45.$

(e) $2\,x^2 + y^2 = 100.$

(f) $x^2 + 4\,y^2 = 1.$

(g) $4\,x^2 + 5\,y^2 = 20.$

(h) $50\,x^2 + y^2 = 200.$

2. Write the equations of the following ellipses and sketch:

(a) Major axis 8, foci at $(\pm 2, 0)$.

(b) Minor axis 10, foci at $(0, \pm 3)$.

(c) Major axis 18, foci at $(0, \pm 3\sqrt{6})$.

(d) Minor axis $2\sqrt{3}$, foci at $(\pm\sqrt{3}, 0)$.

3. Find the equation of an ellipse with center at the origin and foci on the x-axis if (a) a focus bisects the semimajor axis; (b) the distance between the foci equals the minor axis.

4. Find the equation of the ellipse with center at the origin and axes on the coördinate axes which passes through $(1, 3)$ and $(4, 2)$.

5. Find the locus of the midpoints of the ordinates of the circle $x^2 + y^2 = 36$.

6. Find the length of the double ordinate (latus rectum) through a focus of the ellipse $x^2/a^2 + y^2/b^2 = 1$.

7. Write the equation of the parabola with vertex at the origin which passes through the ends of the double ordinate through the right focus of the ellipse $x^2 + 5\,y^2 = 20$.

8. Find the locus of a point which moves so that the sum of its distances from $(0, \pm 8)$ is 20.

9. A semielliptic arch is 40 feet long across the base and 15 feet high with the major axis horizontal. Find the distance from the level of the top to a point on the arch (a) 10 feet from the minor axis; (b) 15 feet from the minor axis.

10. The ends of a rod 12 inches long move along two perpendicular lines. Find the loci of its points of trisection.

11. The semiaxes of an ellipse are 3 feet 4 inches and 2 feet, respectively. Find the lengths of those diameters of the ellipse which make angles of 30° and 60°, respectively, with the major axis.

60. Center not at the origin. Let the center of the ellipse be at the point (h, k), and let the major axis be parallel to the x-axis. Draw through (h, k) lines parallel to the x- and y-axes and call these lines the x'- and y'-axes. The equation of the ellipse referred to these axes is, by (9) (Sec. 57),

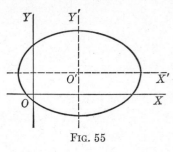

FIG. 55

$$\frac{x'^2}{a^2} + \frac{y'^2}{b^2} = 1.$$

But $x = x' + h$ and $y = y' + k$, or $x' = x - h$ and $y' = y - k$; and this gives

$$\frac{(x - h)^2}{a^2} + \frac{(y - k)^2}{b^2} = 1, \tag{11}$$

if the curve is referred to the x- and y-axes. If the major axis is parallel to the y-axis, the corresponding equation is

$$\frac{(x - h)^2}{b^2} + \frac{(y - k)^2}{a^2} = 1. \tag{12}$$

Since a translation of axes will change equations (11) and (12) into equations (9) and (10), respectively, any equation of the form of equation (11) or (12) represents an ellipse.

61. Theorem. *The equation*

$$Ax^2 + By^2 + Cx + Dy + E = 0 \tag{13}$$

represents an ellipse if A and B are of the same sign.

If A and B are of the same sign, the equation may be written so that both are positive. Completing squares, we may write

$$A\left(x^2 + \frac{C}{A}x + \frac{C^2}{4A^2}\right) + B\left(y^2 + \frac{D}{B}y + \frac{D^2}{4B^2}\right) = \frac{C^2}{4A} + \frac{D^2}{4B} - E.$$

By dividing by the expression in the right member of the equation, we may write the equation in the form of equation (11) or (12) (Sec. 60). Equation (13), therefore, represents an ellipse.

If the quantity $C^2/4\,A + D^2/4\,B - E = 0$, the locus is a **point ellipse**.

If the quantity $C^2/4\,A + D^2/4\,B - E < 0$, there is no real locus.

EXAMPLE. Find the center, semiaxes, foci, and eccentricity of the ellipse $16\,x^2 + 25\,y^2 - 64\,x + 50\,y - 311 = 0$.

Completing squares, we may write

$$16(x^2 - 4\,x + 4) + 25(y^2 + 2\,y + 1) = 400.$$

Dividing by 400 and rearranging, we obtain

$$\frac{(x-2)^2}{25} + \frac{(y+1)^2}{16} = 1.$$

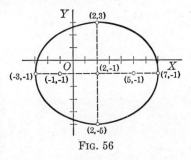

FIG. 56

This equation shows that the center of the ellipse is at $(2, -1)$, that the major axis lies along the line $y = -1$, that the semimajor axis is $a = 5$, and that the semiminor axis is $b = 4$. From $c^2 = a^2 - b^2$ we have $c = 3$. The foci are, therefore, at the points $(-1, -1)$ and $(5, -1)$. The eccentricity is $e = c/a = 3/5$.

62. Scientific applications of the ellipse. The following list is suggestive of the many applications of the ellipse:

(*a*) The planets move in elliptic orbits about the sun with the sun at a focus.

(*b*) The arches of stone and concrete bridges are frequently semi-ellipses.

(*c*) Elliptic gears are used in machines to obtain a slow, powerful movement with a quick return, as in power punches.

(*d*) Whispering galleries usually have elliptical ceilings arranged so that one may stand at a focus. Thus situated he can hear a slight noise made at the other focus, while an individual standing between the foci hears nothing.

(*e*) Because of its graceful beauty the elliptic arch is frequently used in architecture.

(f) The locus of the end of the radius vector which represents the magnetic field in a single-phase induction motor is an ellipse, assuming that the motor is operating at less than synchronous speed. This is the normal condition.

(g) In a certain type of map projection, designed to preserve relative areas, the meridians become arcs of ellipses.

EXERCISES

1. Find the center, semiaxes, and foci of each of the following ellipses and sketch:

(a) $x^2 + 2y^2 + 4x - 16y - 36 = 0$.
(b) $3x^2 + y^2 + 12x + 6y - 3 = 0$.
(c) $x^2 + 9y^2 - 12x - 36y + 36 = 0$.
(d) $5x^2 + 4y^2 - 40x + 40y + 100 = 0$.
(e) $4x^2 + 3y^2 + 8x - 12y = 0$.
(f) $4x^2 + 25y^2 - 20x = 0$.
(g) $2x^2 + y^2 - 10y - 25 = 0$.
(h) $9x^2 + 5y^2 + 36x - 30y + 36 = 0$.

2. Write the equations of the ellipses for which the following conditions are given and sketch:

(a) Major axis 10, foci at $(0, 2)$ and $(8, 2)$.
(b) Major axis 12, foci at $(-1, 1)$ and $(-1, 5)$.
(c) Minor axis 6, foci at $(1, -1)$ and $(7, -1)$.
(d) Minor axis 8, foci at $(4, 3 - 2\sqrt{6})$ and $(4, 3 + 2\sqrt{6})$.

3. Write the equation of the circle which has a diameter coincident with the major axis of the ellipse $25x^2 + 9y^2 - 180y = 0$.

4. Write the equation of the parabola with vertex at the origin which passes through the ends of the minor axis of the ellipse $9x^2 + 16y^2 + 72x = 0$.

5. Write the equation of the ellipse which passes through $(-6, 4)$, $(-8, 1)$, $(2, -4)$, and $(8, -3)$ and which has axes parallel to the coördinate axes.

6. Show that the following equations represent point ellipses or no real loci:

(a) $x^2 + 2y^2 = 0$.   (b) $x^2 + 4y^2 - 2x - 16y + 17 = 0$.
         (c) $3x^2 + y^2 + 12x - 2y + 16 = 0$.

7. The foci of an ellipse are at $(1, 1)$ and $(5, 1)$. The sum of the distances from the foci to any point (x, y) on the ellipse is 8. Find the equation of the ellipse.

8. A point moves so that its distance from $(1, 1)$ is one half of its distance from the line $x + 5 = 0$. Show that the locus is the same ellipse as in Exercise 7.

9. A point moves so that its distance from $(5, 1)$ is one ha'f of its distance from the line $x - 11 = 0$. Show that the locus is the same ellipse as in Exercise 7.

10. What is the eccentricity of the ellipse in Exercise 7?

THE HYPERBOLA

63. Definition and equation of a hyperbola. *A hyperbola is the locus of points the difference of whose distances from two fixed points is a constant.* The two fixed points are called the **foci** of the hyperbola.

Let the distance between the foci be $2\,c$, and let the constant difference be $2\,a$, $(a < c)$. Choose the line through the foci as the x-axis and the point midway between the foci as origin. The coördinates of the foci are $(c, 0)$ and $(-c, 0)$. By definition, we have (Fig. 57)

$$F'P - FP = \pm 2\,a,$$

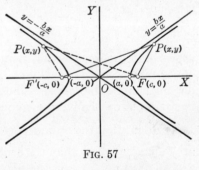

FIG. 57

where the positive sign is used for a point P on the right of the y-axis and the negative sign is used for a point P on the left of the y-axis. But

$$F'P = \sqrt{(x + c)^2 + y^2} \quad \text{and} \quad FP = \sqrt{(x - c)^2 + y^2};$$

hence $\sqrt{(x + c)^2 + y^2} - \sqrt{(x - c)^2 + y^2} = \pm 2\,a.$

Transposing the second radical, squaring, and reducing, we have

$$cx - a^2 = \pm a\sqrt{(x - c)^2 + y^2}.$$

Squaring again and reducing, we may write

$$x^2(c^2 - a^2) - a^2y^2 = a^2(c^2 - a^2).$$

Since $c > a$, let $b^2 = c^2 - a^2$. Making this substitution and dividing by a^2b^2, we obtain the equation of the hyperbola

$$\frac{x^2}{a^2} - \frac{y^2}{b^2} = 1. \tag{14}$$

If the foci are the points $(0, c)$ and $(0, -c)$, the equation of the hyperbola is

$$\frac{y^2}{a^2} - \frac{x^2}{b^2} = 1. \tag{15}$$

Conversely, any equation of the form (14) *or* (15) *represents a hyperbola.* The proof consists in showing that the steps taken in obtaining (14) and (15) can be reversed. The work required involves only simple algebra and will not be set down.

64. Discussion of the equation. We shall now discuss equation (14). The equation shows that the locus is symmetric with respect to both axes and hence is symmetric with respect to the origin. The value of y,

$$y = \pm \frac{b}{a} \sqrt{x^2 - a^2},$$

shows that x^2 cannot be less than a^2; that is, there is no part of the curve between the lines $x = \pm a$. The curve, therefore, does not cross the y-axis. The x-intercepts are $\pm a$. As x increases numerically, the numerical value of y increases. It is evident that the ordinates of the curve, $y = \pm \frac{b}{a}\sqrt{x^2 - a^2}$, are numerically less than the ordinates of the lines $y = \pm \frac{b}{a} x$, respectively, for $x \geqq a$. Hence the curve lies between these two lines.

We shall show next that as x increases indefinitely the difference between the ordinates of the line and curve approaches zero as a limit, that is, that the line is the limiting position of the curve as x increases indefinitely. Because of symmetry it will be sufficient to show this for the first quadrant.

$$\lim_{x \to \infty} \left[\frac{b}{a} x - \frac{b}{a} \sqrt{x^2 - a^2} \right] = \lim_{x \to \infty} \frac{b}{a} \frac{\left[x - \sqrt{x^2 - a^2} \right]\left[x + \sqrt{x^2 - a^2} \right]}{x + \sqrt{x^2 - a^2}}$$

$$= \lim_{x \to \infty} \frac{b}{a} \frac{a^2}{x + \sqrt{x^2 - a^2}} = 0.$$

Hence the curve approaches the line as a limiting position as x and y increase indefinitely.

The hyperbola represented by equation (14), therefore, consists of two parts or branches; one branch is to the right of $x = a$ and between the lines $y = \pm bx/a$, and the other branch is to the left of $x = -a$ and between the same lines. These lines $y = \pm bx/a$ are called the **asymptotes** of the hyperbola. The segment of the line of symmetry through the foci from $(-a, 0)$ to $(a, 0)$, of length $2a$, is called the **transverse axis** of the hyperbola. The segment of the line of symmetry at right angles to the transverse axis, from $(0, -b)$ to $(0, b)$, of length $2b$, is called the **conjugate axis**. The lengths a and b are the **semitransverse** and **semiconjugate** axes, respectively. The point of intersection of the transverse and conjugate axes is the **center**, since the hyperbola is symmetric with respect to this point. The ends of the transverse axis are the **vertices** of the hyperbola.

A similar discussion of equation (15) will show that it represents the same curve with transverse axis along the y-axis.

EXAMPLE. Graph the hyperbola $9 x^2 - 4 y^2 = 36$ and find its foci, semiaxes, and asymptotes.

The equation shows symmetry with respect to both axes. Dividing by 36, we obtain

$$\frac{x^2}{4} - \frac{y^2}{9} = 1.$$

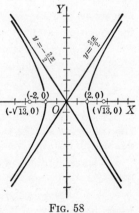

FIG. 58

The equation shows that the transverse axis lies along the x-axis. The semitransverse axis is $a = 2$ and the semiconjugate axis is $b = 3$. The vertices of the hyperbola are at $(\pm 2, 0)$. From $b^2 = c^2 - a^2$ we have $c = \sqrt{13}$. Hence the foci are at $(\pm \sqrt{13}, 0)$. The asymptotes are $y = \pm 3\,x/2$.

65. Eccentricity. Location of foci. The ratio c/a, denoted by e, is called the **eccentricity** of the hyperbola. Since $c^2 = a^2 + b^2$, we may write

$$e = \frac{\sqrt{a^2 + b^2}}{a}.$$

From $c^2 = a^2 + b^2$ we see that c is the hypotenuse of a right triangle with legs a and b, and hence can be easily constructed if the semiaxes are known. The distance c laid off on either side of the center along the transverse axis locates the foci.

EXERCISES

1. Find the semiaxes, eccentricity, foci, and equations of the asymptotes of the following hyperbolas and draw each curve and its asymptotes:

(a) $9\,x^2 - 16\,y^2 = 144$.

(b) $4\,y^2 - 5\,x^2 = 80$.

(c) $3\,x^2 - y^2 = 75$.

(d) $x^2 - 9\,y^2 + 81 = 0$.

(e) $2\,x^2 - 3\,y^2 = 120$.

(f) $45\,y^2 - 4\,x^2 = 180$.

(g) $x^2 - y^2 = 16$.

(h) $x^2 - y^2 = -16$.

2. Write the equations of the hyperbolas for which the following conditions are given and sketch each curve:

(a) Transverse axis 8, foci at $(\pm 6, 0)$.

(b) Transverse axis 6, foci at $(0, \pm 7)$.

(c) Conjugate axis 4, foci at $(\pm 2\sqrt{5}, 0)$.

(d) Conjugate axis $12\sqrt{2}$, foci at $(0, \pm 3\sqrt{10})$.

3. Find the equation of the hyperbola with center at the origin and transverse axis on the x-axis if the distance between the foci is double the distance between the vertices.

4. The asymptotes of a hyperbola are $3\,y = \pm 4\,x$ and the foci are at $(\pm 10, 0)$. Write the equation of the hyperbola.

5. Write the equation of the hyperbola passing through $(4, 6)$ whose asymptotes are $y = \pm\sqrt{3}\,x$.

6. A hyperbola with center at the origin and vertices on the x-axis passes through (3, 1) and (9, 5). Find its equation.

7. A hyperbola with center at the origin and vertices on the y-axis passes through (1, 5) and (4, 10). Find its equation.

8. Find the length of the double ordinate (latus rectum) through a focus of the hyperbola $x^2/a^2 - y^2/b^2 = 1$.

9. Write the equation of the ellipse passing through the origin which has for minor axis the double ordinate through the right focus of the hyperbola $x^2 - 3\,y^2 = 48$. Draw the figure.

10. Find the equation of the locus of a point which moves so that the difference of its distances from $(0, \pm 6)$ equals 4.

66. Center not at the origin. By an argument similar to that used for the ellipse one may show that for the center at (h, k) instead of at the origin the equation of a hyperbola is

$$\frac{(x - h)^2}{a^2} - \frac{(y - k)^2}{b^2} = 1 \tag{16}$$

if the transverse axis is parallel to the x-axis, and is

$$\frac{(y - k)^2}{a^2} - \frac{(x - h)^2}{b^2} = 1 \tag{17}$$

if the transverse axis is parallel to the y-axis. Since a translation of axes will change equations (16) and (17) to equations (14) and (15), respectively, any equation of the form (16) or (17) represents a hyperbola.

67. Theorem. *In general,* the equation

$$Ax^2 + By^2 + Cx + Dy + E = 0 \tag{18}$$

represents a hyperbola if A and B are opposite in sign.

Completing squares, we may write

$$A\left(x^2 + \frac{C}{A}\,x + \frac{C^2}{4\,A^2}\right) + B\left(y^2 + \frac{D}{B}\,y + \frac{D^2}{4\,B^2}\right) = \frac{C^2}{4\,A} + \frac{D^2}{4\,B} - E.$$

Dividing by the expression in the right member of the equation and rearranging, we may write the equation in the form of (16) or (17), since A and B are opposite in sign. Equation (18), therefore, represents a hyperbola.

* See footnote, p. 86.

EXAMPLE. Find the center, semiaxes, asymptotes, foci, and eccentricity of the hyperbola

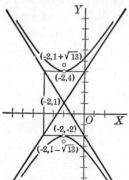

FIG. 59

$$4\,y^2 - 9\,x^2 - 36\,x - 8\,y - 68 = 0.$$

Completing squares, we may write

$$4(y^2 - 2\,y + 1) - 9(x^2 + 4\,x + 4) = 36.$$

Dividing by 36 and rearranging, we obtain

$$\frac{(y-1)^2}{9} - \frac{(x+2)^2}{4} = 1.$$

This equation shows that the center of the hyperbola is at $(-2, 1)$, that the transverse axis lies along the line $x = -2$, that the semitransverse axis is $a = 3$, and that the semiconjugate axis is $b = 2$. From $c^2 = a^2 + b^2$ we have $c = \sqrt{13}$. The foci are, therefore, the points $(-2, 1 + \sqrt{13})$ and $(-2, 1 - \sqrt{13})$. The eccentricity is $e = c/a = \sqrt{13}/3$. The equations of the asymptotes are

$$y - 1 = \pm \tfrac{3}{2}(x + 2),$$

or $3\,x - 2\,y + 8 = 0$ and $3\,x + 2\,y + 4 = 0.$

68. Equilateral hyperbola. In case $a = b$, the hyperbola is called an **equilateral** hyperbola. Equation (14), in that case, reduces to

$$x^2 - y^2 = a^2.$$

The asymptotes have slopes ± 1. If the axes are rotated through an angle of $-45°$, the equation becomes

$$2\,x'y' = a^2. \quad \text{(See Exercise 14, p. 63)}$$

This is the equation of an equilateral hyperbola referred to its asymptotes as axes.

69. Conjugate hyperbolas. Consideration of the two hyperbolas

$$\frac{x^2}{a^2} - \frac{y^2}{b^2} = 1 \quad \text{and} \quad \frac{y^2}{b^2} - \frac{x^2}{a^2} = 1$$

shows that the transverse axis of one is the conjugate axis of the other, and that the same straight lines $y = \pm bx/a$ serve as asymptotes for both curves. Two hyperbolas which are so related are called **conjugate** hyperbolas.

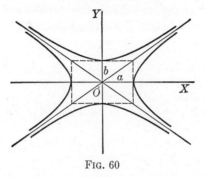

Fig. 60

70. Scientific applications of the hyperbola. The following list is suggestive of the applications of the hyperbola:

(*a*) The equation expressing Boyle's law for a perfect gas under pressure at a constant temperature is of the form of the equation of an equilateral hyperbola referred to its asymptotes as axes.

(*b*) The hyperbola may be used to locate an invisible source of sound, as in locating an enemy's guns or in range-finding. Two listening posts are established and the difference in time of arrival of the report of the gun at the two posts is measured as accurately as possible. The difference in time multiplied by the rate at which sound travels gives the difference in the distances from the two listening posts to the gun. If the two listening posts are used as foci and the difference in distances from the gun as the transverse axis of a hyperbola, then the position of the gun will lie on the hyperbola. A second observation from new positions will give a second hyperbola through the position of the gun. The simultaneous solution of the equations of the two hyperbolas will locate the gun at one of the points of intersection of the two curves. How can one tell at which point of intersection the gun is located?

(*c*) A type of reflecting telescope uses a hyperbolic mirror as the small reflector to reflect the image to the eyepiece.

EXERCISES

1. Find the center, semiaxes, foci, and the equations of the asymptotes of each of the following hyperbolas and sketch:

(a) $x^2 - 3\,y^2 - 4\,x + 18\,y - 50 = 0$.

(b) $16\,x^2 - 9\,y^2 + 96\,x + 72\,y + 144 = 0$.

(c) $4\,x^2 - 5\,y^2 + 8\,x + 40\,y + 4 = 0$.

(d) $3\,x^2 - y^2 - 18\,x - 6\,y = 0$.

(e) $40\,x^2 - 9\,y^2 + 126\,y - 81 = 0$.

(f) $x^2 - y^2 + 8\,x - 7\,y + 6 = 0$.

(g) $9\,x^2 - 4\,y^2 - 36\,x + 24\,y - 36 = 0$.

(h) $4\,x^2 - y^2 - 8\,x + 20 = 0$.

2. Write the equations of the hyperbolas for which the following conditions are given and sketch:

(a) Transverse axis 8, foci at $(0, 2)$ and $(10, 2)$.

(b) Transverse axis 4, foci at $(1, 4)$ and $(1, -4)$.

(c) Conjugate axis 4, foci at $(-2, 3)$ and $(10, 3)$.

(d) Conjugate axis 2, foci at $(1, 0)$ and $(1, 6)$.

3. Write the equation of the ellipse which has its major and minor axes coincident, respectively, with the transverse and conjugate axes of the hyperbola $x^2 - 4\,y^2 - 12\,x = 0$.

4. Show that the eccentricity of the equilateral hyperbola is $\sqrt{2}$.

5. Find the vertices, axes, and foci of the hyperbola $xy = 16$.

6. Write the equations of the hyperbolas conjugate to the following hyperbolas. Sketch each pair of conjugate hyperbolas on the same set of axes with their common asymptotes.

(a) $\dfrac{x^2}{16} - \dfrac{y^2}{9} = 1$.

(b) $\dfrac{x^2}{4} - \dfrac{y^2}{12} = -1$.

(c) $x^2 - y^2 = 10$.

(d) $2\,x^2 - y^2 = 12$.

(e) $xy = 9$.

7. Show that the four foci of two conjugate hyperbolas and the four points of intersection of the tangent lines at the vertices all lie on a circle whose center is the common center of the hyperbolas.

8. Write the equation of the hyperbola which passes through the points $(8, 1)$, $(0, -5)$, $(6, -2)$, and $(2, -2)$, and which has axes parallel to the coördinate axes.

9. The foci of a hyperbola are at $(-8, 1)$ and $(10, 1)$. The difference of the distances from the foci to any point (x, y) on the hyperbola is numerically 6. Find the equation of the hyperbola.

10. A point moves so that its distance from $(-8, 1)$ is three times its distance from the y-axis. Show that the locus is the same hyperbola as in Exercise 9.

11. A point moves so that its distance from $(10, 1)$ is three times its distance from the line $x = 2$. Show that the locus is the same hyperbola as in Exercise 9.

12. What is the eccentricity of the hyperbola in Exercise 9?

CONICS

71. General definition of a conic. *A conic is the locus of a point the ratio of whose distance from a fixed point to its distance from a fixed line is a constant.* The fixed point is called the focus and the fixed line is called the directrix.

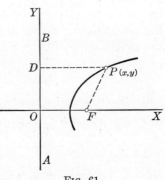

To find the equation of the locus described, let the constant ratio be r, let the directrix, AB, be the y-axis and let the line through the focus, F, perpendicular to the directrix, be the x-axis (Fig. 61). If we call p the distance from AB to F, the coördinates of F are $(p, 0)$. By definition

$$FP = r \cdot DP.$$

Fig. 61

But $\qquad FP = \sqrt{(x-p)^2 + y^2}$ and $DP = x$,

hence $\qquad \sqrt{(x-p)^2 + y^2} = rx,$

or $\qquad x^2(1 - r^2) - 2\,px + y^2 + p^2 = 0.$

If $r = 1$, this equation represents a parabola. (See the theorem of Sec. 55.)

If $r < 1$, this equation represents an ellipse. (See the theorem of Sec. 61.)

If $r > 1$, this equation represents a hyperbola. (See the theorem of Sec. 67.)

It can be shown that the ratio r is the same as the eccentricity defined in Secs. 59 and 65. The proof is left to the student in an exercise in Sec. 73. We shall not discuss the limiting cases where $r \rightarrow 0$ or where $r \rightarrow \infty$.

Because of symmetry of the ellipse and of the hyperbola it is evident that another line and another point could serve as directrix and as focus, respectively, of the ellipse and of the hyperbola. See Exercises 8 and 9, p. 95, and Exercises 10 and 11, p. 103.

72. General second degree equation. The general equation of the second degree in x and y can be written in the form

$$Ax^2 + Bxy + Cy^2 + Dx + Ey + F = 0. \tag{19}$$

It is possible by a proper rotation of axes to obtain an equation of the locus represented by equation (19) in a form which has no xy-term. Rotating the axes through the angle θ by the substitutions

$$x = x' \cos \theta - y' \sin \theta,$$
$$y = x' \sin \theta + y' \cos \theta,$$

and collecting terms, we transform equation (19) into

$$\begin{aligned}
x'^2(A \cos^2 \theta &+ B \sin \theta \cos \theta + C \sin^2 \theta) \\
&+ x'y'[2(C - A) \sin \theta \cos \theta + B(\cos^2 \theta - \sin^2 \theta)] \\
&+ y'^2(A \sin^2 \theta - B \sin \theta \cos \theta + C \cos^2 \theta) \\
&+ x'(D \cos \theta + E \sin \theta) + y'(E \cos \theta - D \sin \theta) \\
&+ F = 0.
\end{aligned}$$

Equating the coefficient of $x'y'$ to zero, we have

$$2(C - A) \sin \theta \cos \theta + B(\cos^2 \theta - \sin^2 \theta) = 0,$$

or $\qquad\qquad (C - A) \sin 2\theta + B \cos 2\theta = 0,$

whence $\qquad\qquad\qquad \tan 2\theta = \dfrac{B}{A - C}. \qquad (A \neq C)$

In case $A = C$, we have $\cos 2\theta = 0$ and hence $\theta = 45°$. There is a value of θ for which $\tan 2\theta$ is equal to any given value. Therefore it is always possible to choose an angle through which to rotate the axes, and eliminate the xy-term in the general second degree equation in x and y. Since the

xy-term can always be removed, we shall have no loss of generality by discussing the equation in the form

$$Ax^2 + Cy^2 + Dx + Ey + F = 0.$$

1. *If the left member of the equation can be factored into two first degree factors, as $(a_1x + b_1y + c_1)(a_2x + b_2y + c_2) = 0$, the equation represents two straight lines* (Sec. 37). These lines may be distinct or coincident.

In case the equation does not represent straight lines, there are four possibilities.

2. *If $A = C$, the equation represents a circle* (Sec. 48).

3. *If either $A = 0$ or $C = 0$, the equation represents a parabola* (Sec. 55).

4. *If A and C have the same sign and $A \neq C$, the equation represents an ellipse* (Sec. 61).

5. *If A and C are opposite in sign, the equation represents a hyperbola* (Sec. 67).

Therefore every second degree equation of the form (19) represents one of the following loci: two straight lines, a circle, a parabola, an ellipse, or a hyperbola. These five types of curves are called **conics**, or **conic sections**, because each can be obtained as a curve of intersection of a plane and a conical surface. They were so studied by the early Greeks.

Equations of types 1, 2, and 4 represent imaginary loci in some cases.

EXAMPLE. Identify the conic

$$11\,x^2 - 24\,xy + 4\,y^2 + 30\,x + 40\,y - 45 = 0.$$

The angle θ through which to rotate the axes into a position parallel to the axes of the conic is found from

$$\tan 2\,\theta = \frac{B}{A - C} = -\frac{24}{7}.$$

If we select for $2\,\theta$ the smallest positive angle with the given tangent, we have $\cos 2\,\theta = -7/25$, from which

$$\sin \theta = \sqrt{\frac{1 - \cos 2\,\theta}{2}} = \frac{4}{5}$$

and

$$\cos \theta = \tfrac{3}{5}.$$

The equations for the required rotation are

$$x = \frac{3\,x' - 4\,y'}{5}, \quad y = \frac{4\,x' + 3\,y'}{5}.$$

These substitutions transform the equation into

$$11\left(\frac{3\,x' - 4\,y'}{5}\right)^2 - 24\left(\frac{3\,x' - 4\,y'}{5}\right)\left(\frac{4\,x' + 3\,y'}{5}\right)$$
$$+ 4\left(\frac{4\,x' + 3\,y'}{5}\right)^2 + 30\left(\frac{3\,x' - 4\,y'}{5}\right)$$
$$+ 40\left(\frac{4\,x' + 3\,y'}{5}\right) - 45 = 0.$$

Simplifying, we obtain

$$x'^2 - 4\,y'^2 - 10\,x' + 9 = 0.$$

This equation shows that the conic is a hyperbola. Completing squares and dividing by 16, we may write

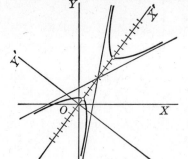

$$\frac{(x' - 5)^2}{16} - \frac{y'^2}{4} = 1.$$

The transverse axis of the hyperbola lies on the x'-axis. The semitransverse axis is $a = 4$ and the semiconjugate axis is $b = 2$. With reference to the new axes the center is at $(5, 0)$ and the vertices are at $(1, 0)$ and $(9, 0)$. The value of c is found to be $2\sqrt{5}$ and the eccentricity $e = \sqrt{5}/2$. The foci are at $(5 \pm 2\sqrt{5}, 0)$. The asymptotes are $y' = \pm \frac{1}{2}(x' - 5)$. The figure shows the relation of the curve to both sets of axes. A further simplification of the equation can be effected by a translation of axes.

Fig. 62

73. Identification of a conic without removing the xy-term. If the equation is solved for y, or x, a study of the quantity under the radical and our knowledge of the extent of the conics enable us to identify the locus.

EXAMPLE 1. From $2x^2 + 2xy + y^2 = 9$, we have
$$y = -x \pm \sqrt{9 - x^2}.$$
The values of x for which y is real are $-3 \leqq x \leqq 3$. For such values of x, the value of y is limited. Therefore the equation represents an ellipse, since the curve lies in a bounded part of the plane.

EXAMPLE 2. From $x^2 - 2xy + y^2 + x - 2y = 0$, we have
$$y = x + 1 \pm \sqrt{1 + x}.$$
The values of x for which y is real are $x \geqq -1$. Therefore, the equation represents a parabola, since the parabola is the only conic which extends to infinity in one half-plane without doing so also in the opposite half-plane.

EXAMPLE 3. From $x^2 + 6xy + y^2 = 2$, we have
$$y = -3x \pm \sqrt{8x^2 + 2}.$$
The values of y are real and unlimited as x increases numerically. Therefore the equation represents a hyperbola.

If when solved for y and simplified, the value of y is rational in x, the equation is factorable and represents two straight lines.

EXAMPLE 4. Identify and draw the curve represented by
$$x^2 - xy + y^2 = 3.$$

Solving as a quadratic in y, we have

$$y = \frac{x}{2} \pm \frac{1}{2}\sqrt{3(4 - x^2)}.$$

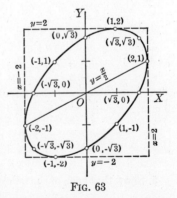

FIG. 63

This equation shows that for a value of x there are two values of y, giving points at equal vertical distances above and below the corresponding point on the line $y = x/2$. That is, the line $y = x/2$ bisects the system of chords drawn parallel to the y-axis. A study of the quantity under the radical shows that the curve lies between the lines

$x = \pm 2$. For such values of x, the value of y is limited. Hence the equation represents an ellipse. It may be necessary to plot a few points, since the curve is not symmetric in the ordinary sense to the line $y = x/2$. The curve is shown in the figure.

EXERCISES

1. Write the equations of the conics for which the following conditions are given:

(a) Focus $(2, 1)$, directrix the y-axis, $r = 1$.
(b) Focus $(1, 2)$, directrix the line $x + 2\,y = 1$, $r = 1$.
(c) Focus $(2, 0)$, directrix the line $x + 6 = 0$, $r = \frac{1}{3}$.
(d) Focus $(1, 1)$, directrix the line $x + y + 4 = 0$, $r = \frac{1}{2}$.
(e) Focus $(0, 3)$, directrix the line $y + 2 = 0$, $r = \frac{3}{2}$.
(f) Focus $(2, -2)$, directrix the line $x - y + 2 = 0$, $r = 2$.

2. Remove the xy-term by rotation of axes, identify, and sketch the following conics:

(a) $9\,x^2 - 24\,xy + 16\,y^2 - 20\,x - 15\,y = 0$.
(b) $9\,x^2 + 24\,xy + 16\,y^2 - 20\,x + 15\,y - 100 = 0$.
(c) $41\,x^2 - 24\,xy + 34\,y^2 - 15\,x - 20\,y = 0$.
(d) $15\,x^2 + 6\,xy + 15\,y^2 - 6\sqrt{2}\,x - 6\sqrt{2}\,y - 34 = 0$.
(e) $x^2 + 2\sqrt{3}\,xy - y^2 = 18$.
(f) $xy + 3\,x - 4\,y = 8$.
(g) $5\,x^2 - 4\,xy + 8\,y^2 - 14\,x - 16\,y + 17 = 0$.
(h) $3\,x^2 + 2\sqrt{3}\,xy + y^2 + 4\,x - 4\sqrt{3}\,y + 16 = 0$.

3. Draw the conics identified in Examples 1, 2, and 3, Sec. 73.

4. Identify and draw the following conics without removing the xy-term:

(a) $3\,x^2 + 2\,xy + y^2 - 8 = 0$.
(b) $3\,x^2 + 2\,xy - y^2 - 8 = 0$.
(c) $x^2 - 2\,xy + y^2 - 4\,x = 12$.
(d) $4\,x^2 - 4\,xy + y^2 - 3\,x + 6\,y = 45$.
(e) $5\,x^2 - 4\,xy + y^2 - 16\,x + 8\,y = 16$.
(f) $xy - 2\,x + 3\,y = 22$.
(g) $5\,x^2 + 4\,xy + 4\,y^2 = 36$.
(h) $9\,y^2 - 6\,xy - 8\,x^2 + 12\,x - 36\,y + 72 = 0$.

5. Show that each of the following equations represents two lines:

(a) $2\,x^2 + 3\,xy - 2\,y^2 - 5\,y - 2 = 0$.
(b) $x^2 - 2\,xy + y^2 + x - y - 2 = 0$.
(c) $x^2 - 2\,xy + y^2 = 0$.

(d) $x^2 - 2x - 8 = 0$.

(e) $x^2 + 4xy + 4y^2 - 2x - 4y + 1 = 0$.

(f) $xy + 2x - 3y - 6 = 0$.

6. Find the equation of the conic through the points $(3, 0)$ $(0, -5)$, $(2, 1)$, $(2, -2)$, and $(-3, -2)$.

7. Identify the conics represented by the loci in Exercises 11–20, inclusive, page 58.

8. Show that the ratio, r, of Sec. 71 is the same as e of Secs. 59 and 65.

MISCELLANEOUS EXERCISES

1. Identify the conics represented by the following equations:

(a) $3x^2 + 3y^2 - 6x + 12y - 16 = 0$.

(b) $2x^2 - 5x + y + 2 = 0$.

(c) $x^2 + 2y^2 - 8x - 16y + 64 = 0$.

(d) $4x^2 - 3y^2 + 4x - 3y = 0$.

(e) $x = 2y^2 - 5y - 3$.

(f) $x^2 - y^2 - x - y = 0$.

2. Identify the conics represented by the following equations:

(a) $x^2 + 2xy + y^2 + x + 2y = 0$.

(b) $2x^2 + 2xy + y^2 - 9 = 0$.

c) $x^2 + 6xy + y^2 - 4 = 0$.

(d) $x^2 - 2xy + y^2 + 4x - 4y = 0$.

3. What conic is represented by each pair of equations

$$y = \pm \frac{b}{a} \sqrt{2ax - x^2} \text{ and } y = \pm \frac{b}{a} \sqrt{x^2 - 2ax}?$$

4. Show that the equation $(x - a)(y - b) = c$ represents an equilateral hyperbola. What are the equations of its asymptotes?

5. Show that the equation $x^{\frac{1}{2}} + y^{\frac{1}{2}} = a^{\frac{1}{2}}$ represents an arc of a parabola. Find its vertex, focus, and directrix. (*Hint.* Rationalize the equation.)

6. Find the points of intersection of the curves $xy = 1$ and $x^2 - 2xy + y^2 - 8x - 8y - 16 = 0$ and check graphically.

7. Find the vertices of the square inscribed in the ellipse $x^2 + 4y^2 = 8x$.

8. Write the equation of the ellipse the ends of whose minor axis are at the foci of the hyperbola $9x^2 - 16y^2 = -144$ and whose eccentricity is the reciprocal of the eccentricity of the hyperbola.

9. Show that the vertices of the convex hexagon, $(-\frac{1}{4}, 0)$, $(0, 1)$, $(6, 5)$, $(12, 7)$, $(6, -5)$, and $(2, -3)$, lie on a parabola with axis along the x-axis. Show that the pairs of opposite sides of the hexagon meet in three points which lie on a straight line.

10. Any two perpendicular lines are drawn through the vertex of a parabola. Show that the line joining their other intersections with the parabola intersects the axis of the parabola in a fixed point.

11. Chords are drawn through an end of the major axis of the ellipse $b^2x^2 + a^2y^2 = 2\,ab^2x$. Find the locus of their midpoints.

12. Lines are drawn through the ends of the minor axis of the ellipse $b^2x^2 + a^2y^2 = a^2b^2$ intersecting in a point on the ellipse. Show that the product of their intercepts on the x-axis is a^2.

13. Two fixed lines intersect at an angle $\tan^{-1} k$. Show that the locus of a point, the product of whose distances from the fixed lines is constant, is a hyperbola.

14. If 2ϕ is the angle between the asymptotes of a hyperbola, show that $\sec\phi = e$, where e is the eccentricity.

15. If e and e' are the eccentricities of conjugate hyperbolas, show that $e^2 + e'^2 = e^2e'^2$.

16. Show that the distance from the center to a point on an equilateral hyperbola is a mean proportional between the focal distances of the point.

17. Let P be any point on a hyperbola. Show that the product of the distances from the asymptotes to P is constant.

18. If a line is drawn intersecting a hyperbola, show that the two segments of the line included between the hyperbola and its asymptotes are equal.

19. Lines are drawn through the vertices of an equilateral hyperbola intersecting in a point on the hyperbola. Show that the bisector of the angle formed by these lines is parallel to an asymptote.

20. The base of a triangle is fixed in length and position. Find the locus of its vertex if the tangents of the base angles have (*a*) a constant sum; (*b*) a constant difference; (*c*) a constant product; (*d*) a constant quotient.

CHAPTER VI

OTHER TYPES OF CURVES IN RECTANGULAR COÖRDINATES

74. Algebraic and transcendental curves. Equations (in rectangular coördinates) whose members can be expressed by a finite number of the operations of addition, subtraction, multiplication, and division of the variables are called **algebraic.** The equations $y^2 = x^3$, $x^2 + y^2 = 4$, and $y = (x - 1)/(x + 1)$, for example, are algebraic equations. Equations which cannot be so expressed are called **transcendental.** The equations $y = e^x$, $y = \log x$, and $x + \sin x = y^2$, for example, are transcendental equations. The graph of an algebraic equation in two variables is called an **algebraic curve,** and the graph of a transcendental equation in two variables is called a **transcendental curve.** Curves in a plane represented by algebraic equations of degree greater than two, or by transcendental equations, are called **higher plane curves.** The curves discussed in Chapters VI, VII, and VIII are higher plane curves, with a few exceptions, and are grouped into chapters according to the method of treatment.

ALGEBRAIC CURVES

75. Illustrations. EXAMPLE 1. Discuss and graph

$$y^2 = (x - 1)(x - 2)(x - 3).$$

The equation shows the locus to be symmetric with respect to the x-axis. The x-intercepts are 1, 2, and 3. For $x = 0$, $y^2 = -6$, and hence the curve does not intersect the y-axis. For $x < 1$, each factor in the right member is negative and there is no real value for y. For $1 < x < 2$, the first factor is positive and the other two are negative, y^2 is therefore positive and there are two real values of y. For $2 < x < 3$, y^2 is negative and there are no real values for y. For $x > 3$, there

111

are real values for y. As x increases indefinitely y increases without limit. Assigning a few values to x between 1 and 2 and values to x greater than 3 we find a few points on the curve, such as $(\frac{5}{4}, .5+)$, $(\frac{3}{2}, .6+)$, $(\frac{7}{4}, .5-)$, $(4, 2.4+)$, and $(5, 4.9-)$. The curve is shown in Fig. 64.

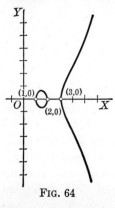

FIG. 64

EXAMPLE 2. Discuss and graph

$$y = \frac{x(x-1)}{(x+1)(x-3)}.$$

There is no symmetry. The curve passes through the origin and has an additional x-intercept, $x = 1$. As x approaches -1 from the left y approaches $+\infty$, and as x approaches -1 from the right y approaches $-\infty$. As x approaches 3 from the left y approaches $-\infty$, and as x approaches 3 from the right y approaches $+\infty$. The lines $x = -1$ and $x = 3$ are, therefore, vertical asymptotes of the curve. Dividing the numerator by the denominator, we have

$$y = 1 + \frac{x+3}{x^2 - 2x - 3},$$

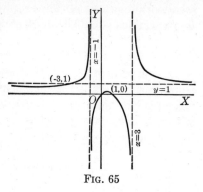

FIG. 65

which shows that as x increases numerically y approaches 1, since $(x+3)/(x^2 - 2x - 3)$ approaches zero.* For $x > 3$,

---

* A convenient method of finding the limit of a rational fraction as the variable becomes infinite is to divide numerator and denominator by the highest power of the variable which occurs and then evaluate the limit. For example,

$$\lim_{x \to \infty} \frac{x+3}{x^2 - 2x - 3} = \lim_{x \to \infty} \frac{\frac{1}{x} + \frac{3}{x^2}}{1 - \frac{2}{x} - \frac{3}{x^2}} = 0,$$

since each of the quantities $\frac{1}{x}, \frac{2}{x}, \frac{3}{x^2}$ approaches zero as x becomes infinite.

$(x+3)/(x^2-2x-3)$ is positive, and therefore $y > 1$. For $x = -3$, $y = 1$. For $x < -3$, $(x+3)/(x^2-2x-3)$ is negative, and therefore $y < 1$. Hence the line $y = 1$ is an asymptote which the curve approaches from above toward the right and from below toward the left. The curve is composed of three branches. One branch is below the asymptote $y = 1$ at the left and remains between the x-axis and the line $y = 1$ until x reaches -3, where it crosses the line $y = 1$ and rises indefinitely as it approaches the line $x = -1$. Another branch is on the right of the line $x = -1$ below the x-axis, goes through the origin, recrosses the x-axis at $x = 1$, and goes indefinitely downward as it approaches the asymptote $x = 3$. A third branch is on the right of the asymptote $x = 3$ and above the x-axis, comes downward and approaches the asymptote $y = 1$ without crossing it. Plotting the points with abscissas -5, -4, -2, 2, 4, 5, and 6, drawing the asymptotes $y = 1$, $x = -1$, and $x = 3$, and indicating the intercepts on the axes, we have enough guides to draw the curve as shown in Fig. 65.

76. Graphing by composition of ordinates. It is sometimes possible to draw more easily the graph of a function by breaking it up into parts, graphing each part separately and combining the graphs. The method is illustrated by graphing the equation $y = x + 1/x$.

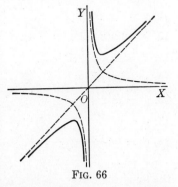

Let $y_1 = x$ and $y_2 = 1/x$, then $y = y_1 + y_2$. Graph $y_1 = x$ and $y_2 = 1/x$ on the same axes. Then add the ordinates corresponding to the same abscissas and the result will be the ordinate of $y = y_1 + y_2 = x + 1/x$.

In a similar manner the graph of a product may be found by

FIG. 66

graphing each factor and taking the product of the ordinates corresponding to the same abscissas. A quotient of two functions can be graphed in a similar manner.

EXERCISES

(The student should reread carefully Sec. 39 before attempting to discuss the graphs of the following equations.)

Discuss and draw the graphs of the following equations:

1. (a) $y = x(x - 3)^2$;   (b) $y^2 = x(x - 3)^2$.

2. (a) $y = x^2(x - 3)$;   (b) $y^2 = x^2(x - 3)$.

3. (a) $y = x(x - 1)(x - 2)(x - 3)$;
      (b) $y^2 = x(x - 1)(x - 2)(x - 3)$.

4. Discuss the graph of the equation $y = (x - a)(x - b)(x - c)$ in each of the following cases: (a) $a < b < c$;   (b) $a < b = c$;   (c) $a = b = c$.

5. Discuss the graph of the equation $y^2 = (x - a)(x - b)(x - c)$ in each of the following cases: (a) $a < b < c$;   (b) $a < b = c$;   (c) $a = b < c$;   (d) $a = b = c$.

Discuss and draw the graphs of the following equations:

6. (a) $y = x^3(x - 5)$;   (b) $y^2 = x^3(x - 5)$.

7. (a) $y^2 = x^4 - 16 x^2$;   (b) $y^2 = 16 x^2 - x^4$.

8. (a) $y^2 = 4(x - 5)/x$;   (b) $y^2 = 4(5 - x)/x$.

9. $y = x(x + 2)/(x - 2)$.

10. $y = 2 x(x + 1)/(x^2 - 4)$.

11. $y^2 = (1 + x)/(1 - x)$.

12. $y^2 = x^2(x + 2)/(x - 2)$.

13. $y^2 = x^2(2 + x)/(2 - x)$.

14. $y^2 = (x^2 - 1)/(x - 3)^2$.

15. $y^2 = 1/x(x - 2)^2$.

16. $y = x/(x^3 - 8)$.

17. $y^3 = x^3/(x^3 - 8)$.

18. $x^2y^2 = 9(x^2 + y^2)$.

19. $y^2 = x^4(x + 5)$.

20. $x^3 + y^3 = x^2y$.

21. $y^2 = x^3 - 1/x^2$.

22. $y^2 = 1/x - 1/x^2$.

23. Discuss the graph of $y = 1/(x - a)(x - b)(x - c)$ in each of the following cases: (a) $a < b < c$;   (b) $a < b = c$;   (c) $a = b = c$.

24. Discuss the graph of $y^2 = 1/(x - a)(x - b)(x - c)$ in each of the following cases: (a) $a < b < c$;   (b) $a < b = c$;   (c) $a = b < c$;   (d) $a = b = c$.

Sketch the graphs of the following equations by the method suggested in Sec. 76:

25. $y = x^2 + 1/x$.

26. $y = x/2 + 1/x^2$.

27. $y = x - 1/x$.

28. $y = 1/x + 1/x^2$.

29. $y = 1 + 2/x + 1/x^2$.

30. $y = x \pm \sqrt{9 - x^2}$.

31. $y = x \pm \sqrt{x^2 - 4}$.

32. $y = 2x \pm 3\sqrt{x}$.

33. $y = 2x + 4 \pm \sqrt{6 + x}$.

34. $y = x - 2 \pm \sqrt{16 - x^2}$.

35. $25 y^2 + 24 xy + 16 x^2 - 400 = 0$. (*Hint.* Solve for y in terms of x.)

TRANSCENDENTAL CURVES

77. The trigonometric functions $\sin x$, $\cos x$, and $\tan x$. From trigonometry we know that as x increases from 0 to $\pi/2$, $\sin x$ varies from 0 to 1; as x increases from $\pi/2$ to π, $\sin x$ varies from 1 to 0; as x increases from π to $3\pi/2$, $\sin x$ varies from 0 to -1; as x increases from $3\pi/2$ to 2π, $\sin x$ varies from -1 to 0; as x increases from 2π to 4π, $\sin x$ goes through the same cycle of values as when x increases from 0 to 2π. We find exactly how $\sin x$ varies by consulting a table of sines. The curve $y = \sin x$ is represented in Fig. 67. The function $\cos x$ goes through the same cycle of

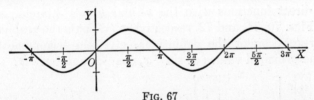

Fig. 67

values as $\sin x$, starting with the value 1 at $x = 0$. The curve $y = \cos x$ is shown in Fig. 68. The function $\tan x$ varies from

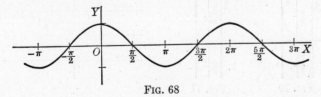

Fig. 68

$-\infty$ to $+\infty$ as x increases from $-\pi/2$ to $\pi/2$, and again as x increases from $\pi/2$ to $3\,\pi/2$, etc. (See Fig. 69.) The graphs of the functions $\sin x$, $\cos x$, and $\tan x$ show that the smallest periods of these functions are $2\,\pi$, $2\,\pi$, and π, respectively.

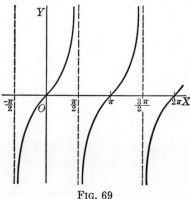

Fig. 69

78. Inverse trigonometric functions. Since the equations $y = \sin^{-1} x$, $y = \cos^{-1} x$, and $y = \tan^{-1} x$ are equivalent to the equations $x = \sin y$, $x = \cos y$, and $x = \tan y$, respectively, the inverse trigonometric functions graph like the corresponding direct functions with the x- and y-axes interchanged. See Figs. 70, 71, and 72, respectively. What is the graphical interpretation of the definitions, given in trigonometry, of the principal values of $\sin^{-1} x$, $\cos^{-1} x$, and $\tan^{-1} x$?

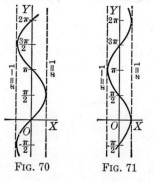 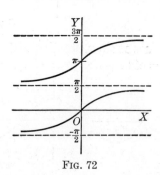

Fig. 70   Fig. 71   Fig. 72

EXERCISES

Sketch the graphs of the following equations:

1. $y = 2 \sin x.$

2. $y = \sin 2\, x.$

3. $y = \sin \dfrac{x}{2}.$

4. $y = \cos 3\, x.$

5. $y = \cos \dfrac{3\, x}{2}.$

6. $y = \cos \dfrac{x}{3}.$

7. $y = \cos (x - \pi/4).$

8. $y = \cos (x + \pi/3).$

9. $y = \cos (2\, x + \pi/4).$

10. $y = \tan (x + \pi).$

11. $y = \sin^2 x.$

12. $y^2 = \sin x.$

13. $y = \sin^3 x.$

14. $y^3 = \sin x.$

15. $y = \sin x^2.$

16. $y = \tan 2\, x.$

17. $y = \tan^2 x.$

18. $y = \sec x.$

19. $y = \csc x.$

20. $y = \cot x.$

21. $y = \sin \pi x.$

22. $y = \sin \dfrac{\pi}{x}.$

23. $y = \sec^{-1} x.$

24. $y = \csc^{-1} x.$

25. $y = \sin^{-1} 2\, x.$

26. $y = \cos^{-1} \dfrac{x}{2}.$

Graph the following equations, using the idea of Sec. 76:

27. $y = \sin x + \cos x.$

28. $y = \sin x - \cos x.$

29. $y = \sin 2\, x + \cos x.$

30. $y = \cos 2\, x + \sin x.$

31. $y = \cos x - \frac{1}{2} \sin 2\, x.$

32. $y = \sin x - \frac{1}{2} \cos 2\, x.$

33. $y = x + \sin x.$

34. $y = x + \sin 2\, x.$

35. The graph of the equation $y = a \sin (bx + c)$, if a, b, and c are constants, is called a sine curve. Show that

(a) the height of an arch, or wave, is a;

(b) the period is $2\, \pi/b$;

(c) the equation $y = k \cos (mx + n)$ can be reduced to the form $y = a \sin (bx + c)$. (*Hint.* $\cos \theta = \sin (\pi/2 - \theta)$.)

36. Show that the equation $y = k_1 \sin mx + k_2 \cos mx$ can be reduced to the form $y = a \sin (bx + c)$.

37. Draw the graph of $y = \sin 2\, x + \sqrt{3} \cos 2\, x$ (a) by the method of Sec. 76; (b) after changing to the form $y = a \sin (bx + c)$.

79. The exponential function $y = a^x$ $(a > 0)$. The curve crosses the y-axis at $y = 1$, but does not cross the x-axis. There are no values of x for which y is negative or zero, and hence the curve is entirely above the x-axis. For further discussion it is necessary to distinguish the cases where $a > 1$, $a = 1$, and $a < 1$.

For $a > 1$, as x increases through positive values y increases very rapidly. Hence the curve turns away from the x-axis

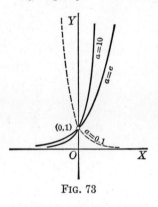

FIG. 73

much more rapidly, in the first quadrant, than it recedes from the y-axis. For x negative, y is less than 1. As x approaches $-\infty$, y approaches 0. The curve, therefore, approaches the x-axis as an asymptote as x approaches $-\infty$.

In case $a = 1$, $y = 1$ for every x and the curve is a straight line.

Since $a^x = (1/a)^{-x}$, it follows that for $0 < a < 1$ the curve is symmetric with respect to the y-axis to the curve $y = a_1^x$, where $a_1 = 1/a$. In Fig. 73, the curve $y = a^x$ is shown for $a = e = 2.718 \cdots$, for $a = 10$, and for $a = 0.1$.

80. Scientific applications of the exponential function. The exponential relation occurs frequently and in many fields.

(*a*) Bacterial growth is according to an exponential law.

(*b*) Some chemical actions, such as the conversion of sugar under certain conditions, follow an exponential law.

(*c*) Radium decomposes according to an exponential law.

(*d*) The friction of a rope around a post, automobile braking, and a slipping belt involve an exponential law.

(*e*) Newton's law of cooling is exponential.

(*f*) The relation between atmospheric pressure and the height above the surface of the earth is exponential.

(*g*) The growth of current immediately after closing a circuit with constant electromotive force, resistance, and inductance is exponential.

(*h*) The amplitude of a damped vibration under certain restrictions decreases according to an exponential law.

(*i*) If we think of interest as being compounded continuously the amount is an exponential function of the time. For this reason the law expressed by an exponential relation is often called the "compound interest law."

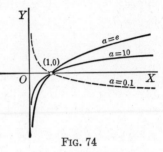

Fig. 74

81. The logarithmic function $y = \log_a x \ (a > 1)$. Since $y = \log_a x$ is equivalent to $x = a^y$, the graph of the logarithmic function will be like that of the exponential function with the *x*- and *y*-axes interchanged. The broken curve in Fig. 74, representing $y = \log_{0.1} x$, illustrates the case $0 < a < 1$.

82. The graph of $y = e^{-x} \sin \pi x$. We draw the graphs of the equations $y_1 = e^{-x}$, $y_2 = \sin \pi x$, and $y_3 = -e^{-x}$ (Fig. 75). For integral values of *x*, $\sin \pi x = 0$, hence the curve $y = e^{-x} \sin \pi x$ crosses the *x*-axis at each point whose abscissa is an integral value of *x*. For $x = (4n+1)/2$ (*n* an integer) $\sin \pi x = 1$, and the value of *y* coincides with the value of y_1. And for $x = (4n+3)/2$ (*n* an integer) $\sin \pi x = -1$, and the value of *y* coincides with the value

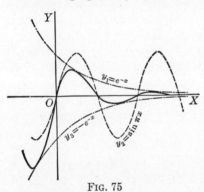

Fig. 75

of y_3. For $0 < \sin \pi x < 1$, $y < y_1$, and for $-1 < \sin \pi x < 0$, $y > y_3$. Hence the curve $y = e^{-x} \sin \pi x$ lies between the curves $y_1 = e^{-x}$ and $y_3 = -e^{-x}$, touching the curve $y_1 = e^{-x}$ whenever $\sin \pi x = 1$ and touching the curve $y_3 = -e^{-x}$ whenever $\sin \pi x = -1$. The ordinate *y* for any abscissa is the product of the ordinates y_1 and y_2 for the same abscissa.

EXERCISES

Sketch the graphs of the following equations:

1. $y = 2^x$.
9. $y = (0.1)^x$.
17. $y = \log_{10}(x^2 - 1)$.

2. $y = 2^{-x}$.
10. $y = 10^{1/x}$.
18. $y = \log_{10}(1 - x^2)$.

3. $y = e^x$.
11. $y = \log_5 x$.
19. $y = x \cdot 2^x$.

4. $y = e^{x^2}$.
12. $y = \log_5 2\, x$.
20. $y = x^2\, 2^x$.

5. $y = 3^x$.
13. $y = \log_e x$.
21. $y = (e^x + e^{-x})/2$.

6. $y = (1/3)^x$.
14. $y = \log_e x^2$.
22. $y = (e^x - e^{-x})/2$.

7. $y = e^{2x}$.
15. $y = \log_{10}(x + 1)$.
23. $y = x \log_{10} x$.

8. $y = e^{x/2}$.
16. $y = \log_{10}(x^2 + 1)$.
24. $y = (\log_{10} x)/x$.

25. $y = e^{-\frac{t}{10}} \cos \pi t$.
26. $y = e^{\frac{t}{10}} \cos \pi t$.

MISCELLANEOUS EXERCISES

Sketch the graphs of the following equations:

1. $y = \dfrac{8\,a^3}{x^2 + 4\,a^2}$ (the witch).

2. $y^2 = \dfrac{x^3}{2\,a - x}$ (the cissoid).

3. $y^2 = \dfrac{x^2(a - x)}{a + x}$ (the strophoid).

4. $y = \dfrac{a}{2}\left(e^{\frac{x}{a}} + e^{-\frac{x}{a}}\right)$ (the catenary).

5. $y = e^{-x^2}$.

6. $\dfrac{x^2}{a^2} + \left(\dfrac{y}{b}\right)^{\frac{2}{3}} = 1$.

7. $y^2 = x(x - 1)^2(x + 2)(x - 2)$.

8. $y = \dfrac{\sin x}{x}$.

9. $y = x \sin \dfrac{\pi}{x}$.

10. $y = (1 + x)^{\frac{1}{x}}$.

11. $y = \log_{10} \dfrac{x - 1}{x + 1}$.

12. $y^2 = x^2 \sin x$.
13. $y^2 = x \sin x$.
14. $\sin^2 y = \sin x \sin \dfrac{x}{3}$.

Graph on the same set of axes and estimate the coördinates of the points of intersection:

15. $y = e^{-x}$, $y = x$.
16. $y = \log_{10} x$, $y = -x$.

17. $y = \log_{10} x$, $y = 10^{-x}$.

Determine from the graph the value of x for which y is zero:

18. $y = x + e^x$.   **19.** $y = 10^x - 2 \cdot 10^{-x}$.

20. Show that the curves $y = \log_a nx$ $(n \neq 0)$ have the same shape as the curve $y = \log_a x$. What is the relation of the curves $y = \log_a x^n$ to the curve $y = \log_a x$?

21. What is the general shape of the graph of $y = a_0 x^n + a_1 x^{n-1} + a_2 x^{n-2} + \cdots + a_{n-1}x + a_n$ (n a positive integer)?

22. In the equation of the catenary, Exercise 4, solve for x in terms of y.

23. Solve the equation $x = \log_e (y + \sqrt{y^2 \pm 1})$ for y in terms of x and graph. (See Exercises 21, 22, Sec. 82).

24. Find the equation of the locus of a point which moves so that the product of its distances from two fixed points is a constant. Call the distance between the fixed points $2\,c$ and the constant a^2. (This curve is called the oval of Cassini.)

25. What does the equation of the locus in Exercise 24 become if $a = c$? (This curve is called the lemniscate of Bernoulli.)

26. Draw on the same axes the ovals of Cassini for $a = 5$, $c = 4$; $a = 4$, $c = 4$; $a = 3$, $c = 4$.

27. If P is a point on the line $5\,x - 2\,y + 4 = 0$ and the origin is at O, find the equation of the locus of Q, a point on OP such that $OP \cdot OQ = 16$. Draw the line and the locus of Q on the same axes. Show that the line and the locus of Q intersect on the circle $x^2 + y^2 = 16$.

28. If P is a point on the parabola $y^2 = 2\,px$ with vertex at O, find the equation of the locus of Q, a point on OP such that $OP \cdot OQ = p^2$.

29. If P is a point on the ellipse $x^2/a^2 + y^2/b^2 = 1$ with center at O, find the equation of the locus of Q, a point on OP such that (a) $OP \cdot OQ = a^2$; (b) $OP \cdot OQ = b^2$. How are the new loci related to the circles $x^2 + y^2 = a^2$ and $x^2 + y^2 = b^2$?

30. If P is a point on the hyperbola $x^2/a^2 - y^2/b^2 = 1$ with center at O, find the equation of the locus of Q, a point on OP such that $OP \cdot OQ = a^2$.

CHAPTER VII

PARAMETRIC EQUATIONS

83. Parameters. It is sometimes convenient to express the rectangular coördinates of a point in terms of a third variable, or parameter.* Each rectangular coördinate is expressed in terms of the auxiliary variable and hence two equations are necessary to represent a locus. These equations are called parametric equations of the locus. The elimination of the parameter between the two equations gives the equation in x and y. For example, the equations $y = t + 2$, $x = t^2 + 2t$

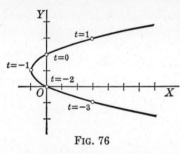

FIG. 76

represent the curve shown in the accompanying figure. Points on the curve are found by assigning values to the parameter t and calculating the coördinates x and y from the given equations. Eliminating the parameter, we have $x = y^2 - 2y$. The curve is a parabola.

An equation in x and y may be replaced by two parametric equations in an unlimited number of ways. It is sufficient to express one of the coördinates, x or y, in terms of a parameter in any way we choose, substitute in the equation and solve for the other coördinate in terms of the parameter. The equations for x and y thus obtained are parametric equations of the same locus as that defined by the equation in x and y. For example, if we put $y = t + 1$ in the equation $x = y^2 - 2y$, we obtain $x = t^2 - 1$. Hence $x = t^2 - 1$, $y = t + 1$ is another parametric representation of the same parabola graphed in Fig. 76.

* The word "parameter" is used to mean either an auxiliary variable or an arbitrary constant.

Parameters are frequently used in deriving equations of loci. Often the parameter is time or a geometric quantity, such as an angle. It should be observed that the locus is independent of the parameter used.

84. Parametric equations of a circle. If we look upon the circle (Fig. 77) as traced by the point $P(x, y)$ moving continuously around the circumference, we may choose $\angle XOP = \theta$ as the parameter and write

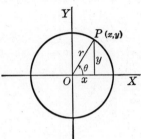

$$x = r \cos \theta \quad \text{and} \quad y = r \sin \theta. \quad (1)$$

FIG. 77

These are parametric equations of a circle with center at the origin.

Squaring and adding the equations (1), we have

$$x^2 + y^2 = r^2(\sin^2 \theta + \cos^2 \theta) = r^2.$$

This is the rectangular equation of a circle with center at the origin and radius r. This equation and the parametric equations represent the same circle.

If we suppose that the point P moves at a constant rate, so that OP turns through an angle ω each second, then at the end of t seconds $\theta = \omega t$. Substituting this value for θ in equations (1), we have

$$x = r \cos \omega t \quad \text{and} \quad y = r \sin \omega t.$$

The parametric equations in the latter form enable us to locate the position of the point P in terms of the time during which it has been moving.

85. Parametric equations of an ellipse. Two circles with centers at the origin have radii a and b $(a > b)$. A line is drawn from O cutting the outer circle at A and the inner circle at B. The line AN is drawn parallel to the y-axis and the line BD is drawn parallel to the x-axis. The lines AN and BD intersect at P. We shall show that the locus of P is an ellipse.

From the figure we have for the coördinates of P

$$x = ON = a \cos \phi \quad \text{and} \quad y = NP = MB = b \sin \phi.$$

Dividing by a and b, respectively, squaring and adding, we have

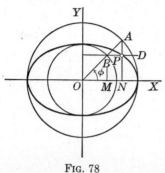

$$\frac{x^2}{a^2} + \frac{y^2}{b^2} = \sin^2 \phi + \cos^2 \phi = 1.$$

This equation represents an ellipse with semiaxes a and b. Hence

$$x = a \cos \phi,$$
$$y = b \sin \phi$$

are parametric equations of an ellipse.

Fig. 78

86. The path of a projectile. Let us assume that no forces other than the attraction of the earth and the initial impulse affect the motion of the projectile. Choose the horizontal and vertical lines through the point at which the projectile leaves the propelling apparatus as the x- and y-axes, respectively.

Call the initial velocity v_0, the angle the initial direction makes with the horizontal α, and the measure of the attraction of the earth g. If g is expressed in feet, then x, y, and v_0 must be expressed in feet.

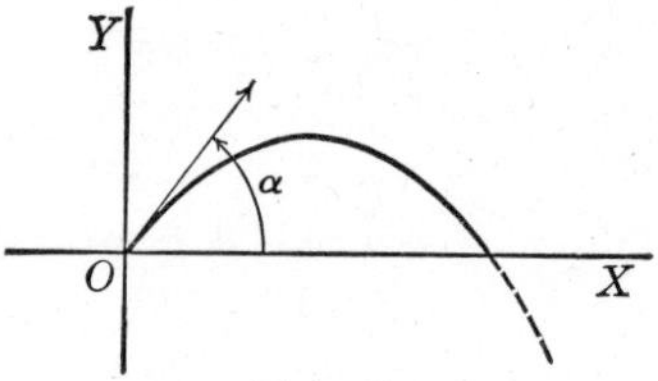

Fig. 79

The horizontal component of the initial velocity is $v_0 \cos \alpha$, and the vertical component is $v_0 \sin \alpha$. The horizontal distance traveled by the projectile in t seconds will be $v_0 t \cos \alpha$, and the vertical distance traveled will be $v_0 t \sin \alpha - \frac{1}{2} g t^2$. The vertical distance is made up of the distance traveled due to the initial velocity minus the distance the attraction of the earth pulls the projectile down. Hence the coördinates of P, after t seconds, will be

$$x = v_0 t \cos \alpha,$$
$$y = v_0 t \sin \alpha - \frac{1}{2} g t^2.$$

These are parametric equations of the path of the projectile. That the path is a parabola is shown by the elimination of the parameter t, which gives

$$y = x \tan a - \frac{gx^2}{2 v_0^2} \sec^2 a.$$

EXERCISES

Draw the graphs of the following curves by giving values to the parameter and computing values of x and y:

1. $x = 1 - t, y = 1 + t.$

2. $x = 3 t, y = t^2.$

3. $x = t^2, y = t - 2.$

4. $x = t, y = t^3.$

5. $x = t^2, y = t^3.$

6. $x = 4 \cos \theta, y = 4 \sin \theta.$

7. $x = \cos 2 \theta, y = \cos \theta.$

8. $x = \theta - \sin \theta, y = 1 - \cos \theta.$

Eliminate the parameter and identify the following curves:

9. $x = 4 \cos \theta, y = 5 \sin \theta.$

10. $x = 3 \cos \theta + 2, y = 4 \sin \theta - 1.$

11. $x = 2 \cos \theta + 3, y = 2 \sin \theta - 1.$

12. $x = \cos \theta + \sin \theta, y = \cos \theta - \sin \theta.$

13. $x = t - 2, y = 2 t^2 - 5 t + 2.$

14. $x = \cos 2 \theta, y = \sin \theta.$

15. $x = \cos \frac{\theta}{2}, y = 1 + \cos \theta.$

16. $x = e^t, y = 4 e^{-t}.$

17. $x = a \sec \theta, y = b \tan \theta.$

18. $x = t + 1/t, y = t - 1/t.$

19. $x = t/(1 + t), y = t^2/(1 + t).$

20. $x = \cos^2 \theta, y = \cos^3 \theta.$

21. Show that $x = \sin^2 \theta, y = 2 \cos \theta$ represent an arc only of the parabola $y^2 = 4 - 4 x$.

Discuss similarly the equations in Exercises 7, 14, 15, and 20.

22. Show that $x = a + bt, y = a' + b't$ represent a straight line with slope b'/b.

23. Draw the line $x = 2 + 3 t, y = 3 + 2 t.$

24. Show that $x = a \cos t + b \sin t, y = a \sin t - b \cos t$ represent a circle. Find its center and radius.

25. Show that $x = a \cos nt + c, y = b \sin nt + d$ represent an ellipse. Find its center and semiaxes.

26. Find the parametric equations of the parabola $y^2 = 2\,px$ if the parameter is the slope of the line joining the origin to the point (x, y) on the parabola.

27. Find parametric equations of a point on the rim of a wheel 6 feet in diameter which turns on its axle at the rate of 30 revolutions per minute if the point starts from (a) the x-axis; (b) the y-axis; (c) the line $y = x$. (*Hint.* Use origin at center of wheel.)

28. What will the equations of the path of a projectile become if the projectile is fired horizontally?

29. A bullet is fired at an angle of elevation of 30° with an initial velocity of 1600 feet per second. Assuming that the bullet leaves the gun at the ground level and that $g = 32$, find how far away the bullet strikes the earth (assumed to be level). How far above the earth is the highest point of its path?

30. If the bullet in the preceding exercise strikes a target 784 feet above the earth, how far away in a horizontal direction is the target from the gun?

31. If a baseball leaves the hand of a pitcher $5\frac{1}{2}$ feet above the ground in a horizontal direction, what must be its initial velocity to cross the plate 18 inches above the ground? Is this a possible velocity?

32. The parametric equations of the path of a projectile are $x = 100\,t$, $y = 100\,t - 16\,t^2$. Plot the path of the projectile.

87. The cycloid.* *The cycloid is the path traced by a fixed point on the circumference of a circle as the circle rolls along a straight line.*

Let the line along which the circle rolls be the x-axis, and let one of the points at which the fixed point on the circle comes in contact with the x-axis be the origin. Choose for the parameter the angle $\theta = \angle ACP$ (measured in radians) in Fig. 80. This is the angle through which the circle, of radius a, has rolled from its position when the point P was at O. The coördinates x and y of P are

$$x = OB = OA - BA = OA - PD,$$
$$y = BP = AD = AC - DC.$$

---

* Galileo (1564–1642) first called attention to the cycloid in 1630, suggesting that it be used for the arches of bridges.

But $OA = $ arc $AP = a\theta$, $PD = a \sin \theta$, $AC = a$,   and $DC = a \cos \theta$. Substituting these values, we have

$$x = a\theta - a \sin \theta = a(\theta - \sin \theta),$$

$$y = a - a \cos \theta = a(1 - \cos \theta),$$

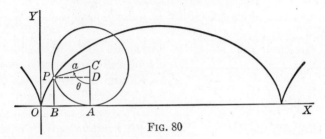

FIG. 80

as parametric equations of the cycloid. Eliminating θ between these equations, we have

$$x = a \cos^{-1} \frac{a - y}{a} - \sqrt{2\,ay - y^2}$$

as the equation in x and y. This is a transcendental equation.

88. Prolate and curtate cycloids. If the point P of the previous section is not on the circumference, the equation of the locus is obtained in a similar manner. Let b represent the distance of the tracing point from the center of the rolling circle. Then the coördinates of the point P are

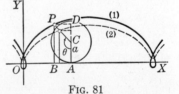

$$x = OA - BA = a\theta - b \sin \theta,$$

$$y = AC - DC = a - b \cos \theta.$$

FIG. 81

If $b > a$, the curve is called a **prolate** cycloid (Fig. 81, curve numbered (1)). If $b < a$, the curve is called a **curtate** cycloid (Fig. 81, curve numbered (2)).

89. Properties of the cycloid. The cycloid has many interesting properties. Some of these properties which can be obtained by more advanced mathematics are:

(a) The length of one arch is $8\,a$, that is, eight times the radius of the rolling circle.

(*b*) The area inclosed between one arch and the *x*-axis is $3\,\pi a^2$, that is, three times the area of the rolling circle.

(*c*) The teeth of gears are often cut with faces which are arcs of cycloids so that there is a rolling contact when the gears are in mesh. The epicycloid, the hypocycloid, and the involute of a circle (discussed in following sections) are also used by the designer of gears.

If the circle rolls along the lower side of the fixed line the cycloid will be inverted, as in Fig. 82, and in this position has the additional properties:

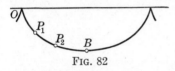

FIG. 82

(*d*) If two particles sliding without friction start from any two points of the curve, P_1 and P_2, at the same time, they will reach the lowest point B at the same instant.

(*e*) A particle sliding without friction will travel from O to B in less time than along any other curve connecting O and B. Hence the cycloid is sometimes called the curve of quickest descent.

The cycloid was the first transcendental curve to be rectified, that is, to have the length of its arc determined by mathematical means.*

EXERCISES

1. Using values of θ at intervals of every 45°, sketch one arch of the cycloid $x = 10(\theta - \sin \theta)$, $y = 10(1 - \cos \theta)$.

2. What are the lengths of the base and altitude of an arch of the cycloid in Exercise 1 ?

3. Derive the equations of the cycloid if the circle rolls along the under side of the fixed line.

4. Derive the equations of the cycloid if the origin is at the top of an arch.

5. Plot the curtate cycloid $x = 9\,\theta - 6 \sin \theta$, $y = 9 - 6 \cos \theta$.

6. Plot the prolate cycloid $x = 9\,\theta - 12 \sin \theta$, $y = 9 - 12 \cos \theta$.

* This was done by Sir Christopher Wren (1632–1723) in 1658.

90. The epicycloid. *If a circle rolls on the outside of another circle in the same plane, a fixed point on the circumference of the rolling circle will trace a path called an epicycloid.*

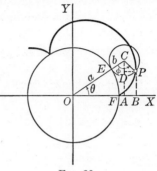

Let a be the radius of the fixed circle and b the radius of the rolling circle. The angle that the line of centers makes with the x-axis will be denoted by θ (Fig. 83) and the angle through which the radius CP turns from the line of centers will be denoted by ϕ ($\phi = \angle OCP$). Then $\angle ACO = \pi/2 - \theta$, and

FIG. 83

$\angle ACP = \phi - (\pi/2 - \theta) = \theta + \phi - \pi/2$. Arcs FE and PE are equal, hence $a\theta = b\phi$. The coördinates of the point P are

$$x = OA + AB = OA + DP = (a+b)\cos\theta + b\sin(\theta + \phi - \pi/2),$$
$$y = BP = AC - DC = (a+b)\sin\theta - b\cos(\theta + \phi - \pi/2).$$

But $\sin(\theta + \phi - \pi/2) = -\cos(\theta + \phi)$, $\cos(\theta + \phi - \pi/2) = \sin(\theta + \phi)$ and $\phi = a\theta/b$. Making these substitutions, we obtain the parametric equations of the epicycloid,

$$x = (a + b)\cos\theta - b\cos\frac{a+b}{b}\theta,$$

$$y = (a + b)\sin\theta - b\sin\frac{a+b}{b}\theta.$$

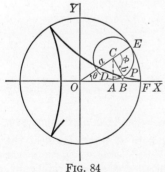

FIG. 84

91. The hypocycloid. *If a circle rolls on the inside of a fixed circle in the same plane, a fixed point on the circumference of the rolling circle traces a curve called a hypocycloid.*

The equations are obtained in a manner similar to that used for the epicycloid and differ from those equations only in the sign of b. Replacing b in the equations of the epicycloid by $-b$, we have the equations of the hypocycloid,

$$x = (a - b) \cos \theta + b \cos \frac{a - b}{b} \theta,$$

$$y = (a - b) \sin \theta - b \sin \frac{a - b}{b} \theta.$$

The special case where $a = 4\,b$ is of interest. The equations become

$$x = 3\,b \cos \theta + b \cos 3\,\theta = b(3 \cos \theta + 4 \cos^3 \theta - 3 \cos \theta)$$
$$= 4\,b \cos^3 \theta = a \cos^3 \theta,$$

$$y = 3\,b \sin \theta - b \sin 3\,\theta = b(3 \sin \theta - 3 \sin \theta + 4 \sin^3 \theta)$$
$$= 4\,b \sin^3 \theta = a \sin^3 \theta.$$

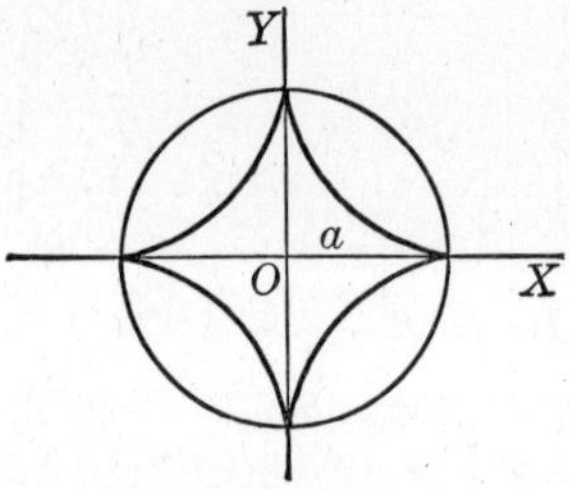

Eliminating θ, we get

$$x^{\frac{2}{3}} + y^{\frac{2}{3}} = a^{\frac{2}{3}}(\cos^2 \theta + \sin^2 \theta),$$

or

$$x^{\frac{2}{3}} + y^{\frac{2}{3}} = a^{\frac{2}{3}},$$

where a is the radius of the fixed circle. This curve is called the hypocycloid of four cusps (Fig. 85).

FIG. 85

EXERCISES

1. Sketch the epicycloid for

(a) $b = \dfrac{a}{3}$;   (b) $b = \dfrac{a}{2}$;   (c) $b = \dfrac{2\,a}{3}$;   (d) $b = a$.

2. Sketch the hypocycloid for

(a) $b = \dfrac{a}{3}$;   (b) $b = \dfrac{a}{2}$;   (c) $b = \dfrac{2\,a}{3}$;   (d) $b = a$.

3. Derive the parametric equations of the hypocycloid directly from a figure.

4. Show that the four-cusped hypocycloid is an algebraic curve.

5. Find the coördinates of the points of intersection of the circle $x^2 + y^2 = 25$ with the epicycloid whose equations are $x = 4 \cos \theta - \cos 4\,\theta$, $y = 4 \sin \theta - \sin 4\,\theta$ and check graphically.

92. The involute of a circle. *If a thread is unwound from*

around a fixed circle, a point on the thread traces a curve called the involute of the circle.

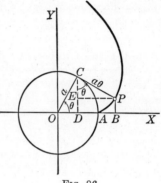

Axes are chosen as indicated in Fig. 86, the point P on the thread having been in contact with the circle at A. The coordinates of P, expressed in terms of θ, give the parametric equations of the involute,

$$x = OD + DB = a \cos \theta + a\theta \sin \theta,$$
$$y = DC - EC = a \sin \theta - a\theta \cos \theta.$$

FIG. 86

MISCELLANEOUS EXERCISES

Eliminate the parameter from the following equations and identify the curves if possible:

1. $x = \sin \dfrac{\theta}{2}$, $y = 1 - \cos \theta$.

2. $x = \tan \theta$, $y = \sin \theta$.

3. $x = 1/t$, $y = 3 t^2$.

4. $x = t \cos t$, $y = t \sin t$.

5. $x = e^t \cos t$, $y = e^t \sin t$.

6. $x = t/(1 + t^2)$, $y = t/(1 - t^2)$.

7. $x = 3 at/(1 + t^3)$, $y = 3 at^2/(1 + t^3)$.

8. $x = 2 \sin \theta$, $y = 3 \cos 2 \theta$.

9. $x = 2 \cos \theta - \cos 2 \theta$, $y = 2 \sin \theta - \sin 2 \theta$.

10. $x = a(1 + \cos \theta)\sin \theta$, $y = a \sin^2 \theta$.

11. $x = a \sin \theta$, $y = b \cos^3 \theta$.

12. $x = \sin t$, $y = \cos 4 t$.

13. Show that $x = \dfrac{a(1 - t^2)}{1 + t^2}$, $y = \dfrac{2 bt}{1 + t^2}$ represent an ellipse.

14. Show that $x = a^t + a^{-t}$, $y = a^t - a^{-t}$ represent an equilateral hyperbola.

15. Show that $x = t^2 + t$, $y = t^2 - t$ represent a parabola.

16. Show that $x = a \log_e t$, $y = \dfrac{a}{2}\left(t + \dfrac{1}{t}\right)$ represent the catenary $y = \dfrac{a}{2}\left(e^{\frac{x}{a}} + e^{-\frac{x}{a}}\right)$.

17. Show that each of the following sets of parametric equations, (1) $x = a \cos^4 t$, $y = a \sin^4 t$, (2) $x = a \sec^4 t$, $y = a \tan^4 t$, and (3) $x = a \tan^4 t$, $y = a \sec^4 t$, represents a different arc of the same parabola.

18. Eliminate θ from the parametric equations of the cycloid.

19. If a ring with polished inner surface is laid on a table and the light shines from one side and above, a brightly illuminated curve is seen on the table within the ring. A similar curve may be observed in a glass of milk. Such a curve is called a caustic. If the ring has a radius of 1, the equations of the caustic are $x = \frac{3}{4} \cos \theta - \frac{1}{4} \cos 3 \theta$, $y = \frac{3}{4} \sin \theta - \frac{1}{4} \sin 3 \theta$. Draw the curve. Show that this curve is an epicycloid for which $a = \frac{1}{2}$ and $b = \frac{1}{4}$.

20. The rod OAB is pivoted at O and hinged at A. The part of the rod OA turns about O at a constant rate, while AB turns about A at a rate twice as great. Find the equations of B if $OA = AB$ and the turning begins when OAB is a straight line.

21. Two perpendicular lines, MN and RS, intersect at O. From a fixed point A on MN a line is drawn cutting RS at B. In either direction from B along AB the distance $BP = BO$ is laid off. The locus of P is called a strophoid. Find its equations.

22. A circle with diameter a is drawn tangent to the x-axis at the origin and cuts the y-axis again at B. Through B the line MN is drawn parallel to the x-axis. A line through the origin cuts the circle at C and MN at D. Lines through C and D parallel to the x- and y-axes, respectively, intersect at P. The locus of P is called the witch of Agnesi. Find the equations of the locus of P.

23. An insect crawls out along the spoke of a wheel 4 feet in diameter at the rate of 1 foot per minute. The wheel is rolling along the ground at the rate of 2 revolutions per minute. Find the equations of the path of the insect. Draw the graph showing the path of the insect for the first 2 minutes.

24. A crank OP, 2 feet in length, turns around O at a uniform rate. A rod 6 feet long is attached at P and the other end Q moves along a fixed line OB. Find the equations of the path of P, and the equations of the path of Q, if the origin is at O and the line OB is the x-axis.

25. The parallelogram $OQPQ'$ is hinged and OQ and OQ' turn about O at constant rates. Find the equations of the locus of P.

CHAPTER VIII

POLAR EQUATIONS

93. Polar coördinates. Another method of locating a point P in a plane is obtained by giving its distance OP (Fig. 87) from a fixed point O and the angle MOP which OP makes with a fixed line through O. The line OM is called the **polar axis**, the line OP is called the **radius vector** of the point P, and the point O is called the **pole**. The polar coördinates of P are designated by (ρ, θ), where ρ is the distance OP and θ is the vectorial angle MOP. The distance ρ is measured from the pole and is considered positive if measured along the

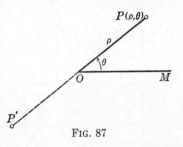

FIG. 87

terminal side of θ, and is considered negative if measured in the opposite direction. Thus in Fig. 87 the point P could be located by giving θ the value of the positive angle MOP' and making ρ negative; or by giving θ the value of the negative angle MOP and making ρ positive.

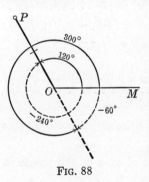

FIG. 88

In Fig. 88 the point P may be represented by any one of the four sets of coördinates — (a) $(2, 120°)$; (b) $(2, -240°)$; (c) $(-2, -60°)$; (d) $(-2, 300°)$ — in which the angle is numerically less than 360°. Any of these angles may be increased or decreased by a multiple of 360° and the point will not be changed. Hence there are an indefinite number of sets of polar coördinates for any point. There is, however, just one point corresponding to a given set of polar coördinates.

Are there four distinct polar representations of a point on the polar axis with θ numerically less than 360°?

94. Relations between rectangular and polar coördinates. If we make the pole of the polar system coincide with the origin of the rectangular system, and place the polar axis on the positive x-axis, it is easy to find relations between the

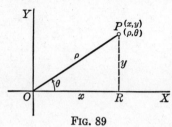

FIG. 89

rectangular coördinates (x, y) and the polar coördinates (ρ, θ) of any point P. From the triangle OPR we have

$$x = \rho \cos \theta, \qquad y = \rho \sin \theta,$$

and

$$\rho = \sqrt{x^2 + y^2}, \qquad \theta = \tan^{-1}\frac{y}{x}.$$

EXERCISES

1. Plot the points $(4, 30°)$; $(4, -30°)$; $(-4, 30°)$; $(-4, -30°)$; $(-3, -60°)$; $(-5, -90°)$; $(4, -45°)$; $(-5, 180°)$; $(-5, -180°)$.

2. Plot the points $(5, \pi/4)$; $(-5, \pi/4)$; $(-5, -\pi/3)$; $(0, 0)$; $(10, \pi/2)$; (a, π); $(-a, -\pi)$; $(0, \pi/4)$; $(a, 2 n\pi)$, where n is any integer.

3. A regular hexagon with sides each 4 units in length has its center at the pole and one vertex on the polar axis. What are the polar coördinates of its vertices?

4. Give at least three more distinct pairs of polar coördinates representing the point $(1, \pi/3)$.

5. Give the rectangular coördinates of each of the points in Exercises 1 and 2.

6. Plot on one diagram $(3, 0)$; $(2\sqrt{3}, \pi/6)$; $(3\sqrt{2}, \pi/4)$; $(6, \pi/3)$; $(2\sqrt{3}, -\pi/6)$; $(-3\sqrt{2}, 3\pi/4)$; $(-6, 2\pi/3)$. Show that these points lie on a straight line perpendicular to the polar axis.

7. Give the polar coördinates of the points whose rectangular coördinates are $(4, 4)$; $(4, -4)$; $(-4, 4)$; $(-4, -4)$; $(0, 2)$; $(2, 0)$; $(1, -3)$; $(-1, -3)$; (h, k).

8. Find the distance between $(5, 2\pi/3)$ and $(8, \pi/3)$. (*Hint.* Use the cosine law.) Check the answer by using rectangular coördinates.

9. Show that $(4, 5\pi/6)$, $(12 - 4\sqrt{3}, \pi/2)$, and $(12, \pi/3)$ lie on a straight line.

10. Find the area of the triangle whose vertices are

(a) $(0, 0)$, $(10, \pi/6)$, $(12, \pi/3)$.
(b) $(4, \pi/3)$, $(6, 2\pi/3)$, $(8, 4\pi/3)$.
(c) $(4, \pi/6)$, $(8, 5\pi/6)$, $(6, -\pi/2)$.
(d) $(10, \pi/6)$, $(8, \pi/2)$, $(5, 5\pi/6)$.

95. Graphs of polar equations. EXAMPLE 1. Draw the graph of $\rho = 2 \sin \theta$.

Assigning values* to θ and finding corresponding values of ρ, we make a table of values:

$\theta =$	$0°$	$30°$	$45°$	$60°$	$90°$	$120°$	$135°$	$150°$	$180°$
$\rho =$	0	1	$\sqrt{2}$	$\sqrt{3}$	2	$\sqrt{3}$	$\sqrt{2}$	1	0

Plotting the corresponding points and drawing a smooth curve through them in the order of increasing θ, we have the graph shown in Fig. 90. It is to be noted that if θ is allowed to vary from 180° to 360°, the corresponding values of ρ will be numerically equal to those obtained above but will be negative. Hence these additional points will coincide with those already found and no new part of the curve will be obtained. The graph is, therefore, completed as θ varies from 0° to 180°.

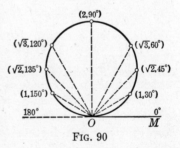

FIG. 90

* The student should not overlook those values of θ for which the trigonometric function under consideration has maximum, zero, or minimum values.

The student can readily check that this curve is a circle by transforming the equation to rectangular coördinates.

EXAMPLE 2. Draw the graph of $\rho = 4(1 + \cos \theta)$.

Making a table of values,

$\theta =$	0°	30°	45°	60°	90°	120°	135°	150°	180°
$\rho =$	8	7.5	6.8	6	4	2	1.2	0.5	0

plotting the corresponding points, and drawing a smooth curve through them in the order of increasing θ, we obtain

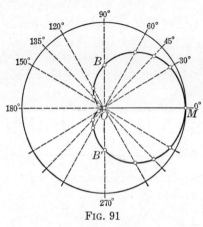

the branch MBO of the curve in Fig. 91. If θ is allowed to vary from 180° to 360° the corresponding values of ρ will be equal, in reverse order, to those obtained above and will be positive. Hence additional points are found and the branch $OB'M$ is drawn.

FIG. 91

EXAMPLE 3. Draw the graph of $\rho = a\theta$.

Assigning positive values (in radian measure) to θ and finding the corresponding values of ρ, we plot points and draw the curve as shown in Fig. 92 for $a = 1$. Since ρ varies directly as θ, ρ will increase indefinitely as θ increases. Hence the curve will recede in spiral form farther and farther from the pole.

The student should draw that part of the graph corresponding to negative values of θ.

Discuss the graph for $a = -1$.

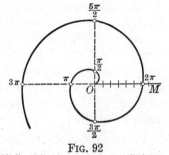

FIG. 92

EXERCISES

Draw the graphs of the following equations:

1. $\rho = 2 \cos \theta.$ 8. $\rho \cos \theta = 3.$ 15. $\rho(2 - \cos \theta) = 1.$
2. $\rho = 4(1 - \cos \theta).$ 9. $\rho = 2 \sin^2 \theta.$ 16. $2 \rho = \theta.$
3. $\rho = 2(1 + \sin \theta).$ 10. $\rho = 4\sqrt{\cos \theta}.$ 17. $\rho = 2 - \theta.$
4. $\rho = 2(1 - \sin \theta).$ 11. $\rho = 2 + 4 \cos \theta.$ 18. $\rho = 4/(1 + \theta^2).$
5. $\rho = 6 \sin \theta.$ 12. $\rho = 4 + 2 \cos \theta.$ 19. $\rho = 4(\sin \theta + \cos \theta).$
6. $\rho = - 10 \cos \theta.$ 13. $\rho = 4 - 2 \cos \theta.$ 20. $\rho = 3 + \sin \theta.$
7. $\rho = 5.$ 14. $\rho = 4 + 2 \sin \theta.$ 21. $\rho = \tan \theta.$

22. $\rho = 4 \sec \theta \tan \theta.$ 23. $\rho = 4 \csc \theta \cot \theta.$

Transform to rectangular coördinates and check the graphs of Exercises 1, 5, 6, 7, 8, 19, 22, 23.

Transform to rectangular coördinates and identify:

24. $\rho^2 = 4 \tan \theta \sec^2 \theta.$ 27. $\rho(1 - \cos \theta) = 1.$
25. $\rho = 2 \tan^2 \theta \sec \theta.$ 28. $\rho(2 - \cos \theta) = 1.$
26. $\rho^2 = 2 \csc 2 \theta.$ 29. $\rho \sin 2 \theta = 2(\sin \theta + \cos \theta).$

Transform to polar coördinates:

30. $x^2 + y^2 = 10 x.$ 32. $x^2 - y^2 = 10 x.$
31. $x^2 + y^2 + 10 y = 0.$ 33. $y^2 = x^4 - x^2.$

34. Verify that $\rho = 2 + \cos \theta$ and $\rho = \cos \theta - 2$ represent the same curve.

35. Why do $\rho = f(\theta),$ $\rho = f(\theta + 2 n\pi)$ for n an integer, and $- \rho = f(\theta + (2 n + 1) \pi)$ represent the same curve?

36. Find other polar equations which represent the same curves as the equations in Exercises 11, 15, 19, and 20.

96. Polar equation of a straight line. In the figure, $OC = p$ is drawn from the pole perpendicular to the line AB whose equation we are seeking and making an angle ω with the polar axis. Let $P(\rho, \theta)$ be any point on the line AB and draw OP. Then $\angle COP = \theta - \omega,$ and from the figure we have

$$\rho \cos (\theta - \omega) = p.$$

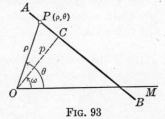

FIG. 93

This is the polar equation of the line AB, since it is a relation between ρ and θ that is true for every point on the line AB and for no other point.

There are some important special cases of the polar equation of the straight line. For a line perpendicular to the polar axis $\omega = 0$ and the equation becomes

$$\rho \cos \theta = p.$$

For a line parallel to the polar axis $\omega = 90°$ and the equation becomes $\rho \cos (\theta - 90°) = p$ or $\rho \sin \theta = p.$

A line through the pole has for its equation

$$\theta = k. \quad (k \text{ a constant})$$

97. Polar equation of a circle. Let (ρ_1, θ_1) be the polar coördinates of the center and (ρ, θ) the polar coördinates of any point on a circle of radius r. Equating the square of the distance from (ρ_1, θ_1) to (ρ, θ) to r^2, we have for the polar equation of a circle

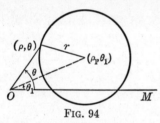

Fig. 94

$$\rho^2 + \rho_1{}^2 - 2\,\rho\rho_1 \cos (\theta - \theta_1) = r^2.$$

The polar equation is, in general, more complicated than the equation of the circle in rectangular coördinates. Some special cases of the equation of the circle in polar coördinates are quite simple and useful.

(a) If the center of the circle is at the pole, then $\rho_1 = 0$ and the equation reduces to

$$\rho = r.$$

(b) If the pole is at the end of a diameter that extends to the right along the polar axis, then $\theta_1 = 0$ and $\rho_1 = r$ and the equation becomes

$$\rho = 2\,r \cos \theta.$$

(c) If the pole is at the end of a diameter that is perpendicular to the polar axis and extends upward, then $\theta_1 = 90°$ and $\rho_1 = r$ and the equation becomes

$$\rho = 2\,r \sin \theta.$$

98. Polar equation of a conic. The polar equation of a conic can easily be obtained from the definition in Sec. 71. Choose the focus for the pole and the line through the focus perpendicular to the directrix for the polar axis. The ratio of the definition is the eccentricity of the conic.

By definition, $FP = eDP$. (Fig. 95)

But $FP = \rho$ and $DP = p + \rho \cos \theta$. Hence

$$\rho = ep + e\rho \cos \theta.$$

Solving for ρ, we have

$$\rho = \frac{ep}{1 - e \cos \theta}.$$

Figs. 96, 97, and 98 are drawn for $e = 1$, $e = \frac{1}{2}$, and $e = 2$, respectively, and represent a parabola, an ellipse, and a hyperbola.

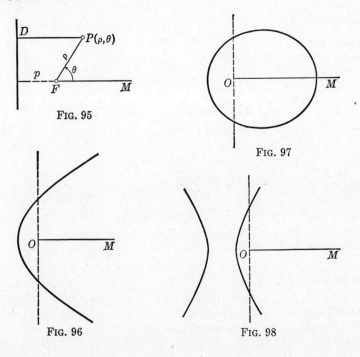

FIG. 95

FIG. 97

FIG. 96

FIG. 98

EXERCISES

1. A line is perpendicular to the polar axis at a point 5 units distant from the pole. Derive its polar equation directly from a figure.

2. A line is parallel to the polar axis and distant 3 units from it. Derive its polar equation directly from a figure.

3. Show that for a line perpendicular to the polar axis and to the left of the pole we may use $\omega = 0°$ or $\omega = 180°$ in the general equation of the line. Similarly for a line parallel to and below the polar axis we may use $\omega = 90°$ or $\omega = 270°$.

4. Draw the following lines:

(a) $\rho \cos \theta = 3$.
(b) $\rho \sin \theta = -1$.
(c) $\theta = \pi/3$.
(d) $\theta = \tan^{-1} \frac{3}{4}$.
(e) $\rho = 2\sqrt{2} \sec (\theta - \pi/4)$.
(f) $\rho = 3 \sec (2\pi/3 - \theta)$.

5. Transform the equations of Exercise 4 to rectangular coördinates.

6. A square of side 5 units has one vertex at the pole and the lower side along the polar axis. Write the equations of the four sides and the two diagonals.

7. Show directly from a figure that $\rho = a \cos \theta$ represents a circle with diameter a.

8. By changing the equation to rectangular coördinates show that $\rho = a \cos \theta$ represents a circle.

9. Prove that $\rho = a \sin \theta$ represents a circle and show its position relative to the pole and the polar axis.

10. Draw the following circles:

(a) $\rho = 10 \cos \theta$.
(b) $\rho = 6 \sin \theta$.
(c) $\rho = -8 \cos \theta$.
(d) $\rho = -4 \sin \theta$.
(e) $\rho = 5$.
(f) $\rho = -5$.

11. Find the locus of the midpoints of all chords passing through a fixed point on a given circle.

12. Derive the equation of the conic if the focus is on the left of the directrix.

13. Derive the equation of the conic if the directrix is parallel to and above the polar axis and the focus is at the pole. How will the equation differ if the directrix is below the polar axis?

14. Graph the following equations:

(a) $\rho = \dfrac{6}{1 - \cos \theta}$.

(d) $\rho = \dfrac{4}{2 + \sin \theta}$.

(b) $\rho = \dfrac{6}{1 - \sin \theta}$.

(e) $\rho = \dfrac{8}{1 + 3 \cos \theta}$.

(c) $\rho = \dfrac{4}{2 + \cos \theta}$.

(f) $\rho = \dfrac{8}{1 + 3 \sin \theta}$.

15. Show that $\rho = a/(\cos \theta + 1)$ and $\rho = a/(\cos \theta - 1)$ represent the same parabola.

16. Show that $\rho = a \sec^2 \dfrac{\theta}{2}$ is a parabola, and sketch.

17. Change $y^2 = 2\,px$ to an equation in polar coördinates.

18. Change $x^2/a^2 + y^2/b^2 = 1$ to an equation in polar coördinates.

19. Change $x^2/a^2 - y^2/b^2 = 1$ to an equation in polar coördinates.

20. Why do the results in Exercises 17, 18, and 19 differ from the general polar equation of the conic developed in the text?

99. The rose-leaved curves $\rho = a \sin n\theta$ and $\rho = a \cos n\theta$. These families of curves are very much alike. We shall discuss the curve $\rho = a \sin 3\,\theta$.

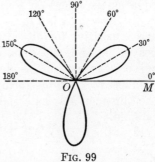

FIG. 99

The radius vector ρ will be zero whenever $3\,\theta$ is $0°$, $180°$, or some multiple of $180°$. This will occur when θ is $0°$, $60°$, $120°$, $180°$, $240°$, $300°$, etc. Numerically ρ will be greatest when $3\,\theta$ is some odd multiple of $90°$, that is, when θ is $30°$, $90°$, $150°$, $210°$, $270°$, $330°$, etc. As θ varies from $0°$ to $30°$, $3\,\theta$ varies from $0°$ to $90°$, $\sin 3\,\theta$ varies from 0 to 1, and ρ varies from 0 to a. As θ varies from $30°$ to $60°$, ρ decreases from a to 0; as θ varies from $60°$ to $90°$, ρ decreases from 0 to $-a$; as θ varies from $90°$ to $120°$, ρ increases from $-a$ to 0; as θ varies from $120°$ to $150°$, ρ increases from 0 to a; and as θ varies from $150°$ to $180°$, ρ decreases from *a* to 0. As θ varies from 180° to 360°, the same curve is retraced. The graph of the equation is shown in Fig. 99.

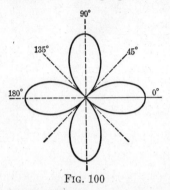

FIG. 100

In case *n* is an even number, the curve will have 2 *n* loops, as is illustrated in Fig. 100 for $\rho = a \cos 2\,\theta$.

100. The limaçon of Pascal.* If to each radius vector of the circle, located with respect to the pole and the polar axis as shown in Fig. 101, is added a positive constant *b*, the locus of *P*, the end of the new radius vector, is a limaçon.

The equation of a circle thus located is (Sec. 97)

$$\rho = 2\,a \cos \theta,$$

where *a* is the radius. The equation of the locus of *P* is evidently

$$\rho = 2\,a \cos \theta + b.$$

(1) If $b > 2\,a$, ρ is always positive and the graph of the equation is shown in Fig. 101 as the curve numbered (1).

(2) If $b = 2\,a$, $\rho = 0$ for $\theta = \pi$ and is positive for other values of θ, and the resulting curve is shown as the curve numbered (2). This form of the limaçon is called the **cardioid**.

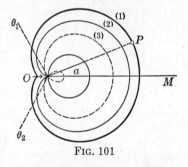

FIG. 101

(3) If $b < 2\,a$, $\rho = 0$ for $\theta_1 = \cos^{-1}(-b/2\,a)$ in the second quadrant and for $\theta_2 = \cos^{-1}(-b/2\,a)$ in the third quadrant, and $\rho < 0$ for values of θ such that $\theta_1 < \theta < \theta_2$. The curve is shown as the curve numbered (3). For $b = a$, the curve is called the **trisectrix**.

* Pascal was a French mathematician who lived from 1623 to 1662.

101. The spirals. The spirals are curves for which the radius vector continuously increases or decreases as the vectorial angle changes. The curve makes a circuit of the pole for each change of 2π in the vectorial angle. The spirals are transcendental curves.

Some of the spirals have names suggested by the fact that the polar coördinates enter into the equation in the same way as rectangular coördinates enter into the equation of the curve for which the spiral is named. For example, the equation $\rho^2 = a\theta$ is called the parabolic spiral. There is no analogy between the loci.

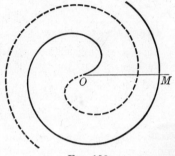

FIG. 102

The spirals can be readily graphed by locating a few points on each turn of the curve about the pole. Fig. 102 shows the graph of $\rho^2 = 4\theta$. Solving for ρ, we have $\rho = \pm 2\sqrt{\theta}$. The solid line represents the part of the curve obtained by using positive values of ρ and the dotted line represents that part of the curve obtained by using negative values of ρ.

EXERCISES

Draw the rose-leaved curves corresponding to the following equations:

1. $\rho = 4 \sin 2\ \theta$.
2. $\rho = 4 \cos 3\ \theta$.
3. $\rho = 3 \sin 4\ \theta$.
4. $\rho = 4\ a \sin \theta$.
5. $\rho = a \cos 4\ \theta$.

6. $\rho = a \cos 5\ \theta$.
7. $\rho = a \sin 6\ \theta$.
8. $\rho = 5\ a \cos 10\ \theta$.
9. $\rho = 5 \sin 2(\theta - \pi/4)$.
10. $\rho = 5 \cos 2(\theta + \pi/4)$.

11. Draw only that part of the graph of $\rho = 3 \sin 2\ \theta$ which is obtained as θ varies from $\pi/4$ to π.

12. Draw only that part of the graph of $\rho = 2 \cos 3\ \theta$ which is obtained as θ varies from $210°$ to $330°$.

Draw the limaçons corresponding to the following equations:

13. $\rho = 1 - 2 \sin \theta$.   17. $\rho = 6 + 3 \cos \theta$.

14. $\rho = 1 + 2 \sin \theta$.   18. $\rho = 6 - 3 \sin \theta$.

15. $\rho = 1 - 2 \cos \theta$.   19. $\rho = 3(1 - \cos \theta)$.

16. $\rho = 1 + 2 \cos \theta$.   20. $\rho = 3(1 + \sin \theta)$.

Graph the following:

21. $\rho = e^{a\theta}$ (logarithmic spiral).   23. $\rho^2 \theta = a$ (lituus).

22. $\rho\theta = a$ (hyperbolic spiral).   24. $(\rho - a)^2 = a^2(1 - \theta^2)$.

Transform to equations in rectangular coördinates:

25. $\rho\theta = a$.   26. $\rho = a \cos 2\,\theta$.   27. $\rho = a(1 - \sin \theta)$.

28. Find the polar equation of the locus of a point P which moves so that the radius vector OP varies directly as the vectorial angle (spiral of Archimedes).

102. The intersection of polar curves.
Care must be exercised in the simultaneous solution of polar equations. It is usually desirable to check the solutions found by solving the equations simultaneously with the solutions found by drawing the two loci on the same diagram. The following example illustrates the difficulty.

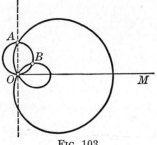

Fig. 103

EXAMPLE. Find the intersections of the curves $\rho = \sin \theta$ and $\rho = 2 \cos \theta + 1$.

Eliminating ρ, we have

$$\sin \theta = 2 \cos \theta + 1.$$

Replacing $\sin \theta$ by $\pm \sqrt{1 - \cos^2 \theta}$, squaring, and solving, we obtain

$$\cos \theta = 0 \quad \text{and} \quad \cos \theta = -\tfrac{4}{5}.$$

For $\cos \theta = 0$, we have from each equation $\rho = 1$ when $\theta = \pi/2$, and $\rho = -1$ and $\rho = 1$, respectively, when $\theta = 3\,\pi/2$. Hence $A(1, \pi/2)$ is an intersection. For $\cos \theta = -\tfrac{4}{5}$, θ in the second quadrant, $\rho = \tfrac{3}{5}$ in one case and $\rho = -\tfrac{3}{5}$ in the other. Hence there is no intersection for this value of θ. For $\cos \theta = -\frac{4}{5}$, θ in the third quadrant, $\rho = -\frac{3}{5}$ in each equation, and the point $B(-\frac{3}{5}, 216° 52')$ is an intersection. The pole should be checked independently, since it is represented by $\rho = 0$ no matter what value θ may have.

In some cases there are points other than the pole at which the curves evidently intersect but whose coördinates are not given by the simultaneous solutions of the equations. The coördinates of these points may be found by using other pairs of equations which represent the same curves. (See Exercises 34, 35, and 36, page 137.)

EXERCISES

Find the points of intersection of the following curves and check graphically:

1. $\rho = 4(1 + \cos \theta)$ and $\rho \cos \theta = 3$.

2. $\rho = a \sin \theta$ and $\rho \sin \theta = a$.

3. $\rho = 4 \sin^2 \theta$ and $\rho = 3$.

4. $\rho = 2 a \cos 2 \theta$ and $\rho = a$.

5. $\rho = a\theta$ and $\rho\theta = a$.

6. $\rho^2 = \tan \theta \sec^2 \theta$ and $\rho = \sqrt{2}$.

7. $(\rho - a)^2 = a^2(1 - \theta^2)$ and $\rho = a\theta$.

8. $\rho = 6 \sin 2 \theta$ and $\rho = 6 \cos 2 \theta$.

9. $\rho = a \sin 6 \theta$ and $\rho = a \cos 3 \theta$.

10. $\rho = a(1 + 2 \cos \theta)$ and $\rho = a \cos \theta$.

11. $\rho = 4 \cos \theta$ and $\rho = 4 \sin \theta$.

12. $\rho^2 = a^2 \sin \theta$ and $\rho = a$.

13. $\rho = a(1 - \cos \theta)$ and $\rho = a \cos \theta$.

14. $\rho = a \cos \theta$ and $\rho = a \sin 2 \theta$.

15. $\rho = 4(1 + 2 \cos \theta)$ and $\rho = 4 \sin \theta$.

16. $\rho = a(1 + \cos \theta)$ and $\rho = a \cos \dfrac{\theta}{2}$.

17. $\rho = a \sin^2 \dfrac{\theta}{3}$ and $\rho = a \sin^3 \dfrac{\theta}{3}$.

18. $\rho = a(1 - \cos \theta)$ and $\rho = a/(1 + \cos \theta)$.

MISCELLANEOUS EXERCISES

1. Draw the curves corresponding to the following equations:

(a) $\rho = 1 - \sin 2\ \theta$.

(b) $\rho = 2 - \sin 2\ \theta$.

(c) $\rho = a^2 \tan^2 \theta \sec \theta$.

(d) $\rho^2 = a^2 \sin 2\ \theta$.

(e) $\rho = 4 \cos \dfrac{3\ \theta}{2}$.

(f) $\rho = 4 \cos \dfrac{2\ \theta}{3}$.

(g) $\rho \sin \dfrac{\theta}{3} = a$.

(h) $\rho = 6 \csc \dfrac{\theta}{2}$.

(i) $(\rho - 4)^2 = \sin^2 \theta$.

(j) $(\rho - 4)^2 = \sin 8\ \theta$.

(k) $\rho = 2 \cos \theta / \cos 2\ \theta$.

(l) $\rho = 2 \sin \theta / \sin 2\ \theta$.

2. Show that $x + y = 5$ and $\rho = 5/(\sin \theta + \cos \theta)$ represent the same line and draw the graph from the polar equation.

3. Show that $\rho^2 \sin 2\ \theta = a$ and $\rho^2 \cos 2\ \theta = a$ each represents an equilateral hyperbola.

Transform into equations in polar coördinates and graph:

4. $y = x/(x^2 + a^2)$.

5. $y^3 = x^3(2 - x)$.

6. $4\ y^2 = 4\ x^2 + x^3$.

7. $(x^2 + y^2)^2 = 2\ x(x^2 - 3\ y^2)$.

8. $x^4 - y^2 + x^2y^2 = 0$.

9. $(x^2 + y^2)^3 = 16\ a^2x^2y^2(x^2 - y^2)^2$.

10. From the parametric equations of the strophoid obtained in Exercise 21, page 132, obtain its polar equation.

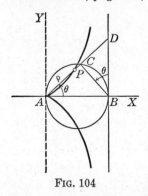

FIG. 104

11. Transform $\rho = 3 \tan \theta$ to Cartesian coördinates and investigate for asymptotes.

12. See Fig. 104. To a circle of radius a, with a diameter AB, a tangent is drawn at B. Any line is drawn from A cutting the circle at C and the tangent at D. The locus of P, where $AP = CD$, is called the cissoid of Diocles. Find its equation.

13. Transform to rectangular coördinates and check that the cissoid has an asymptote as shown in the figure.

14. A moving line segment of variable length has its ends on two fixed perpendicular lines and is at a constant distance from their point of intersection. Find the equation of the locus of its midpoint.

15. See Fig. 105. From a fixed point A, any line AB is drawn cutting a fixed line CD at M. The points P and P' are located so that $P'M = MP = b$, a constant. The locus of P and P' is called the conchoid of Nicomedes. Find its equation.

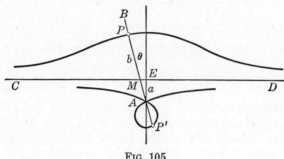

FIG. 105

16. Find the equation of the locus of the vertex of a triangle with a fixed base if the product of the other two sides is equal to the square of one half the base. This curve is the lemniscate of Bernoulli and is illustrated in Fig. 106.

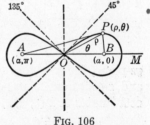

17. A moving line of constant length has its ends on the x- and y-axes. Find the polar equation of the locus of its midpoint.

18. A moving line of constant length has its ends on the x- and y-axes. Find the polar equation of the locus of any fixed point on it.

FIG. 106

19. A moving line of constant length has its ends on the x- and y-axes. Find the polar equation of the locus of the foot of the perpendicular from the origin to the line.

20. If a line is drawn from a fixed point O outside a circle, cutting the circle in the points P and Q, show that $OP \cdot OQ$ is a constant.

21. In a triangle the base AB is a fixed length a. Find the equation of the locus of the vertex C if the exterior angle at B formed by producing AB is $\frac{3}{2} \angle CAB$. (*Hint.* Choose A for the pole and use the law of sines.)

SOLID ANALYTIC GEOMETRY

CHAPTER IX

POINTS, PLANES, AND LINES

103. Rectangular coördinates. In a space of three dimensions a point can be definitely located by giving its directed distances from three mutually perpendicular planes, called coördinate planes. In the figure

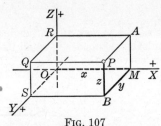

Fig. 107

the three planes XOY, YOZ, and XOZ are called the *xy*-, *yz*-, and *xz*-planes, respectively, and their lines of intersection OX, OY, and OZ are called the *x*-, *y*-, and *z*-axes, respectively. The point O is the origin. The directed distances of a point P from the *yz*-plane, the *xz*-plane, and the *xy*-plane are called the *x*-, *y*-, and *z*-coördinates, respectively, of the point P. Thus the coördinates of $P(x, y, z)$ are represented by

$$x = QP, \qquad y = AP, \qquad z = BP.$$

It is frequently convenient to locate P by drawing

$$x = OM, \qquad y = MB, \qquad z = BP.$$

The three coördinate planes divide space into eight divisions called octants. The octant in which the coördinates are all positive is called the first octant and the others are seldom numbered. They are distinguished by the signs of the coördinates. The student should draw axes and locate the points $(3, 2, 4)$, $(3, -2, 4)$, $(3, 0, 4)$, $(-3, 2, -4)$, and $(-3, -2, 4)$.

148

104. Distance between two points. Drawing lines through $P_1(x_1, y_1, z_1)$ and $P_2(x_2, y_2, z_2)$ parallel to each of the coördinate axes, and other lines as indicated in the figure, we have a rectangular parallelepiped of which the distance between P_1 and P_2 is a diagonal. The length of the diagonal in terms of the sides is

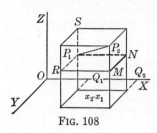

FIG. 108

$$P_1P_2 = \sqrt{P_1N^2 + NM^2 + MP_2^2}.$$

But $P_1N = Q_1Q_2 = x_2 - x_1$, and similarly, $NM = y_2 - y_1$ and $MP_2 = z_2 - z_1$. Hence

$$P_1P_2 = \sqrt{(x_2 - x_1)^2 + (y_2 - y_1)^2 + (z_2 - z_1)^2}.$$

In particular, the distance from the origin $(0, 0, 0)$ to a point $P_1(x_1, y_1, z_1)$ is

$$OP_1 = \sqrt{x_1^2 + y_1^2 + z_1^2}.$$

105. Direction of a line. The direction of a line through the origin is determined if we know the angles it makes with the positive directions of the three coördinate axes. These angles are called the **direction angles** of the line and are denoted by α, β, and γ as the angles made with the x-, y-, and z-axes, respectively. It is found that the cosines of the angles are more useful than the angles, and the direction of a line is usually given by the cosines of its direction angles. The cosines of the direction angles are called the **direction cosines** of the line. If the direction cosines of a line AB are $\cos \alpha$,

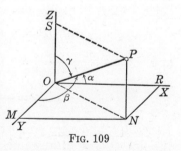

FIG. 109

$\cos \beta$, and $\cos \gamma$, the direction cosines of the line BA are $\cos (180° - \alpha)$, $\cos (180° - \beta)$, and $\cos (180° - \gamma)$.

The direction cosines of a line through the origin are related. In the figure we see that

$$OR = OP \cos \alpha, \quad RN = OM = OP \cos \beta, \quad NP = OS = OP \cos \gamma.$$

Squaring and adding, we have

$$OR^2 + RN^2 + NP^2 = OP^2(\cos^2 \alpha + \cos^2 \beta + \cos^2 \gamma).$$

But $\qquad\qquad OR^2 + RN^2 + NP^2 = OP^2;$

hence $\qquad\qquad \cos^2 \alpha + \cos^2 \beta + \cos^2 \gamma = 1.$

The direction cosines of a line not through the origin are defined to be the same as the direction cosines of a line parallel to the given line and passing through the origin. Thus in Fig. 108 we have

$$\cos \alpha = \frac{P_1 N}{P_1 P_2}, \quad \cos \beta = \frac{P_1 R}{P_1 P_2}, \quad \cos \gamma = \frac{P_1 S}{P_1 P_2},$$

or $\quad \cos a = \frac{x_2 - x_1}{P_1 P_2}, \quad \cos \beta = \frac{y_2 - y_1}{P_1 P_2}, \quad \cos \gamma = \frac{z_2 - z_1}{P_1 P_2}.$

Squaring and adding, we have

$$\cos^2\alpha + \cos^2\beta + \cos^2\gamma = \frac{(x_2 - x_1)^2 + (y_2 - y_1)^2 + (z_2 - z_1)^2}{P_1 P_2{}^2} = 1.$$

This verifies the fact that for any line the sum of the squares of the direction cosines is 1.

Any three numbers a, b, and c (not all zero) are proportional to the direction cosines of some line. Let (a, b, c) be any point P (Fig. 109). We have

$$OP = \sqrt{a^2 + b^2 + c^2},$$

and $\quad \cos a = \frac{a}{\sqrt{a^2 + b^2 + c^2}}, \quad \cos \beta = \frac{b}{\sqrt{a^2 + b^2 + c^2}},$

$$\cos \gamma = \frac{c}{\sqrt{a^2 + b^2 + c^2}}.$$

Hence a, b, and c are proportional to the direction cosines of the line OP, or of any line parallel to OP. The direction cosines of the line joining the origin to any point (x, y, z) are

$$\cos a = \frac{x}{\sqrt{x^2 + y^2 + z^2}}, \quad \cos \beta = \frac{y}{\sqrt{x^2 + y^2 + z^2}},$$

$$\cos \gamma = \frac{z}{\sqrt{x^2 + y^2 + z^2}}.$$

Numbers proportional to the direction cosines of a line are called **direction numbers** of the line. The direction cosines may be obtained from the direction numbers by dividing each number by the square root of the sum of the squares of the three direction numbers.

EXAMPLE. Find the distance between the points $(9, 2, -1)$ and $(-3, 5, -5)$ and the direction of the line through them.

The distance between the points is

$$d = \sqrt{[9 - (-3)]^2 + (2 - 5)^2 + [-1 - (-5)]^2} = \sqrt{169} = 13.$$

Considering the direction of the line as that from the first point to the second, the direction cosines are

$$\cos \alpha = \frac{-3 - 9}{13} = -\frac{12}{13}, \quad \cos \beta = \frac{5 - 2}{13} = \frac{3}{13},$$

$$\cos \gamma = \frac{-5 - (-1)}{13} = -\frac{4}{13}.$$

If we consider the direction of the line as that from the second point to the first, the direction cosines are

$$\cos \alpha = \frac{12}{13}, \quad \cos \beta = -\frac{3}{13}, \quad \cos \gamma = \frac{4}{13}.$$

The numbers $12, -3$, and 4, or any three numbers proportional to them, will serve as direction numbers of the line through the two points.

106. Angle between two lines. Let $P(x, y, z)$ and $P_1(x_1, y_1, z_1)$ be two points and let the direction cosines of OP and OP_1 be $\cos \alpha$, $\cos \beta$, and $\cos \gamma$, and $\cos \alpha_1$, $\cos \beta_1$, and $\cos \gamma_1$, respectively. In the triangle OPP_1 we have

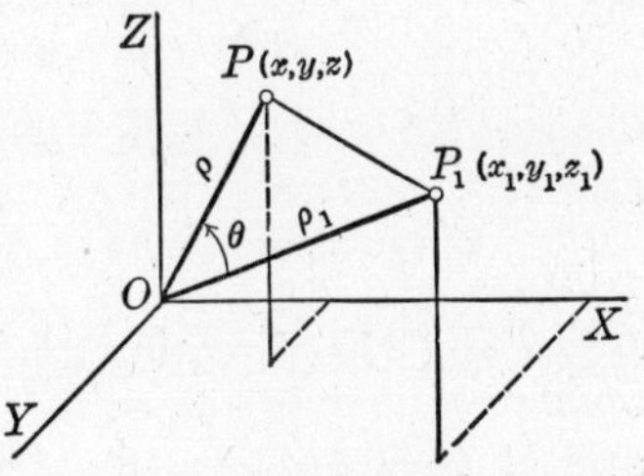

FIG. 110

$$\overline{PP_1}^2 = \rho^2 + \rho_1^2 - 2\rho\rho_1 \cos \theta,$$

$$\text{or} \quad \cos \theta = \frac{\rho^2 + \rho_1^2 - \overline{PP_1}^2}{2\rho\rho_1}.$$

But (Sec. 104) $\rho^2 = x^2 + y^2 + z^2$, $\rho_1^2 = x_1^2 + y_1^2 + z_1^2$, and $\overline{PP_1}^2 = (x - x_1)^2 + (y - y_1)^2 + (z - z_1)^2$.

Making these substitutions and reducing, we have

$$\cos \theta = \frac{xx_1 + yy_1 + zz_1}{\sqrt{x^2 + y^2 + z^2} \cdot \sqrt{x_1^2 + y_1^2 + z_1^2}}.$$

The direction cosines of OP are

$$\cos \alpha = \frac{x}{\sqrt{x^2 + y^2 + z^2}}, \quad \cos \beta = \frac{y}{\sqrt{x^2 + y^2 + z^2}},$$

and
$$\cos \gamma = \frac{z}{\sqrt{x^2 + y^2 + z^2}},$$

and the direction cosines of OP_1 are

$$\cos \alpha_1 = \frac{x_1}{\sqrt{x_1^2 + y_1^2 + z_1^2}}, \quad \cos \beta_1 = \frac{y_1}{\sqrt{x_1^2 + y_1^2 + z_1^2}},$$

and
$$\cos \gamma_1 = \frac{z_1}{\sqrt{x_1^2 + y_1^2 + z_1^2}}.$$

Hence we may write

$$\cos \theta = \cos \alpha \cos \alpha_1 + \cos \beta \cos \beta_1 + \cos \gamma \cos \gamma_1. \qquad (1)$$

If the lines do not pass through the origin or do not intersect, the angle between them is defined to be the same as the angle between lines through the origin parallel to the given lines. Hence the cosine of the angle between any two lines is given in terms of the direction cosines of the two lines by equation (1).

The condition that the two lines are perpendicular is that $\cos \theta = 0$, that is,

$$\cos \alpha \cos \alpha_1 + \cos \beta \cos \beta_1 + \cos \gamma \cos \gamma_1 = 0.$$

EXAMPLE. Find the angle between the line joining the origin to (3, 4, 5) and the line joining the points (2, 1, 4) and (10, 5, 5).

The direction cosines of the first line are $\dfrac{3}{5\sqrt{2}}$, $\dfrac{4}{5\sqrt{2}}$, and $\dfrac{5}{5\sqrt{2}}$, and the direction cosines of the second line are $\frac{8}{9}$, $\frac{4}{9}$, and $\frac{1}{9}$. Hence

$$\cos \theta = \frac{8 \cdot 3 + 4 \cdot 4 + 1 \cdot 5}{9 \cdot 5\sqrt{2}} = \frac{\sqrt{2}}{2},$$

and the angle between the lines is 45°.

EXERCISES

1. Find the length and direction cosines of the line segment drawn from the origin to each of the following points.

(a) (4, 4, 2).   (c) (− 3, − 2, 6).   (e) (0, 5, 0).
(b) (8, 4, − 1).   (d) (4, 2, 0).   (f) (4, 0, 3).

2. Find the length and direction cosines of the line segments joining the following pairs of points:

(a) (− 2, 2, 1) and (4, 5, − 1).
(b) (5, − 2, 3) and (− 3, 6, − 1).
(c) (4, 5, 7) and (− 2, 3, 7).
(d) (10, 9, − 2) and (3, 4, − 3).
(e) (3, 1, 2) and (− 1, − 3, 2).
(f) (− 3, 4, 5) and (7, 4, 5).

3. (a) If $\alpha = \beta = 60°$, find γ (two solutions). (b) If $\alpha = \beta = 30°$, find γ.

4. Draw the line through the origin which has $\cos \alpha = \cos \beta = \sqrt{2}/2$.

5. Find the direction angles of a line which makes equal angles with the coördinate axes.

6. Find the direction cosines of the lines whose direction numbers are

(a) 1, 2, and 2.   (c) 5, 6, and − 8.   (e) 2, 3, and 6.
(b) 2, − 6, and 9.   (d) 1, 1, and 0.

7. Show that the points (1, − 2, 3), (− 4, − 6, 1), and (11, 6, 7) lie on a straight line.

8. Find the points on the x-axis which are 7 units distant from the point (2, 3, 6).

9. Find the equation of the locus of points in the yz-plane which are 7 units distant from the point (2, 3, 6).

10. Find the equation of the locus of all points which are 7 units distant from the point (2, 3, 6).

11. Find the angle between the line through (5, − 1, 7) and (1, − 3, 3) and a line having $\cos \alpha = \frac{11}{15}$, $\cos \beta = \frac{2}{3}$, and $\cos \gamma = \frac{2}{15}$.

12. Find the angle between a line whose direction numbers are 2, − 1, and 0 and the line through (2, 3, − 2) and (− 5, − 2, − 6).

13. Show that the line through (1, 5, 8) and (3, 2, 4) is (a) parallel to the line through (0, 0, 0) and (− 4, 6, 8); (b) perpendicular to the line through (− 1, 9, − 2) and (− 7, 1, 1).

154   SOLID ANALYTIC GEOMETRY

14. Show in two ways that the points (*a*) (5, 1, 5), (4, 3, 2), and (− 3, − 2, 1) are the vertices of a right triangle; (*b*) (3, 7, − 2), (− 1, 8, 3), and (− 3, 4, − 2) are the vertices of an isosceles triangle; (*c*) (4, 2, 4), (10, 2, − 2), and (2, 0, − 4) are the vertices of an equilateral triangle.

15. Show that the midpoint of the line segment joining (x_1, y_1, z_1) and (x_2, y_2, z_2) is
$$\left(\frac{x_1 + x_2}{2}, \ \frac{y_1 + y_2}{2}, \ \frac{z_1 + z_2}{2}\right).$$

107. Equation of a plane. Let ON be the line from the origin perpendicular to the plane, and let its length be p and

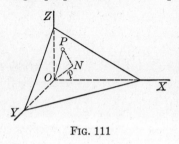

Fig. 111

its direction cosines be $\cos \alpha_1$, $\cos \beta_1$, and $\cos \gamma_1$. Let $P(x, y, z)$ be any other point in the plane, and let the direction cosines of OP be $\cos \alpha$, $\cos \beta$, and $\cos \gamma$. The triangle ONP is a right triangle for all points P which lie in the plane and for no other points. We have

$$p = ON = OP \cos \theta. \quad (\theta = \angle NOP)$$

But $\cos \theta = \cos \alpha \cos \alpha_1 + \cos \beta \cos \beta_1 + \cos \gamma \cos \gamma_1$, $\cos \alpha = x/OP$, $\cos \beta = y/OP$, and $\cos \gamma = z/OP$. Making these substitutions and reducing, we have

$$x \cos \alpha_1 + y \cos \beta_1 + z \cos \gamma_1 = p \qquad (2)$$

as the equation of a plane, in which the constants are the length and the direction cosines of the perpendicular from the origin to the plane. The length p is positive when measured from the origin to the plane.

Conversely, any equation of the form of equation (2) *represents a plane.*

By retracing the steps by which equation (2) is obtained, we see that equation (2) is satisfied by the coördinates of points P for which the angle ONP is a right angle, and by the coördinates of no other points. All such points lie in a plane. Hence any equation in the form of (2) represents a plane.

108. Theorem. *The equation*

$$Ax + By + Cz + D = 0 \qquad (3)$$

represents a plane, provided that A, B, and C are not all zero.

Transposing D and dividing by $\pm \sqrt{A^2 + B^2 + C^2}$, we have

$$\frac{A}{\pm\sqrt{A^2 + B^2 + C^2}}x + \frac{B}{\pm\sqrt{A^2 + B^2 + C^2}}y$$

$$+ \frac{C}{\pm\sqrt{A^2 + B^2 + C^2}}z = \frac{-D}{\pm\sqrt{A^2 + B^2 + C^2}}. \quad (4)$$

By Sec. 105, the quantities

$$\frac{A}{\pm\sqrt{A^2+B^2+C^2}}, \quad \frac{B}{\pm\sqrt{A^2+B^2+C^2}}, \text{ and } \frac{C}{\pm\sqrt{A^2+B^2+C^2}}$$

are the direction cosines of a line. Equation (4) is, therefore, in the form of equation (2), and hence equation (3) represents a plane perpendicular to the line whose direction cosines are

$$\cos \alpha_1 = \frac{A}{\pm\sqrt{A^2 + B^2 + C^2}}, \quad \cos \beta_1 = \frac{B}{\pm\sqrt{A^2 + B^2 + C^2}},$$

$$\cos \gamma_1 = \frac{C}{\pm\sqrt{A^2 + B^2 + C^2}}.$$

The distance p from the origin to the plane measured along the normal is

$$p = \frac{-D}{\pm\sqrt{A^2 + B^2 + C^2}},$$

where the sign before the radical is chosen so that p is positive.

Planes parallel to coördinate axes or parallel to coördinate planes have equations which are special cases of equation (3).

In case a plane is parallel to a coördinate axis, say the x-axis, the direction angle made by the normal with that axis is 90° and the corresponding direction cosine, $\cos \alpha_1$, is zero. Hence, in equation (3), $A = 0$. Similarly, the equation of a plane parallel to the y-axis has no y-term, and a plane parallel to the z-axis has no z-term. Thus the equations

$$2y - 3z = 5, \quad x + 7z - 2 = 0, \quad 3x + 2y + 4 = 0$$

represent planes parallel to the x-, y-, and z-axes, respectively.

In case a plane is parallel to a coördinate plane, the normal is at right angles to the two axes lying in that coördinate plane. Hence two direction cosines are zero. The only variable in the equation of such a plane is the one corresponding to that axis to which the given plane is perpendicular. Thus the equations $2x = 7, \quad y + 3 = 0, \quad z = 9$ represent planes parallel to the yz-, the xz-, and the xy-planes, respectively.

EXAMPLE. Discuss the locus of the equation

$$2x + 3y + 4z = 12.$$

The equation represents a plane since it is of first degree. Direction numbers of the normal to the plane are 2, 3, and 4. The direction cosines are found from the direction numbers to be $\cos \alpha_1 = 2/\sqrt{29}$, $\cos \beta_1 = 3/\sqrt{29}$, and $\cos \gamma_1 = 4/\sqrt{29}$.

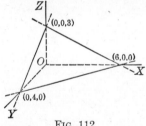

FIG. 112

The distance from the origin to the plane is $12/\sqrt{29}$. The intercepts on the x-, y-, and z-axes are 6, 4, and 3, respectively.

The lines in which the plane intersects the coördinate planes are called the **traces** of the plane.

In the xy-plane, $z = 0$. Hence, to find the equation of the trace in the xy-plane set $z = 0$ in the equation of the plane. Similarly, to find the xz-trace set $y = 0$, and to find the yz-trace set $x = 0$. The equations of the xy-, yz-, and xz-traces of the plane under discussion are

$$2x + 3y = 12, \quad 3y + 4z = 12, \quad x + 2z = 6,$$

respectively. The traces and intercepts are shown in Fig. 112.

109. To find the equation of a plane satisfying given conditions. Planes are usually determined by three given points or by the direction of the normal and one point.

In case three points are given, substitute their coördinates in turn in equation (3). We thus obtain three equations from which three of the numbers A, B, C, and D may be determined in terms of the fourth. Or, by dividing each of the equations by one of the numbers, say A, we have three equations in the unknowns B/A, C/A, and D/A which may be solved simultaneously.

EXAMPLE 1. Find the equation of the plane through the points $(1, 1, 1)$, $(-2, -1, 2)$, and $(3, 9, 3)$.

Equation (3) may be divided by D* and written

$$A'x + B'y + C'z + 1 = 0,$$

where $A' = A/D$, $B' = B/D$, and $C' = C/D$. The equations expressing the condition that the points are in the plane are

$$A' + B' + C' + 1 = 0,$$
$$-2A' - B' + 2C' + 1 = 0,$$
$$3A' + 9B' + 3C' + 1 = 0.$$

Solving simultaneously, we have $A' = -\frac{1}{2}$, $B' = \frac{1}{3}$, and $C' = -\frac{5}{6}$. Substituting these values and reducing, we have the desired equation,

$$3x - 2y + 5z - 6 = 0.$$

In case the direction of the normal and one point are given, we may use equation (3). The numbers A, B, and C are direction numbers of the normal to the plane. From the given direction of the normal we obtain direction numbers which are used for A, B, and C; and D is determined so that the plane passes through the given point.

EXAMPLE 2. Find the equation of the plane through the point $(3, 5, -1)$ perpendicular to the line through $(-1, 3, 7)$ and $(4, 2, 5)$.

Direction numbers of the line through the given points are 5, -1, and -2. Hence we may take $A = 5$, $B = -1$, $C = -2$, and write

$$5x - y - 2z + D = 0$$

---

* Division must be by a quantity not zero. In case $D = 0$, it will be impossible to solve the set of conditional equations. In such a case, we should have to divide by one of the other numbers.

as the equation of a plane perpendicular to the given line. Substituting the coördinates of the point $(3, 5, -1)$, we find the value of D, $D = -12$, for which the plane passes through the given point. The required equation is, therefore,

$$5\,x - y - 2\,z - 12 = 0.$$

EXERCISES

1. Find the intercepts on the axes and the traces in the coördinate planes of each of the following planes, and sketch the portion of each plane which is intercepted by the coördinate planes:

(a) $2\,x + 3\,y + 6\,z = 14$.   (c) $11\,x + 10\,y - 2\,z = 20$.
(b) $x - y - 5\,z + 9 = 0$.   (d) $4\,x - y + z = 8$.

2. Find the distance from the origin to each of the planes in Exercise 1.

3. Sketch the following planes:

(a) $x + 2\,y = 4$.   (e) $x + y = 0$.   (i) $y = -3$.
(b) $2\,y - z = 6$.   (f) $2\,z = x$.   (j) $z = k$.
(c) $2\,x - 3\,y = 8$.   (g) $z = ky$.   (k) $z^2 = 4$.
(d) $x - y = 0$.   (h) $x = 5$.   (l) $x^2 - 2\,x - 3 = 0$.

4. Picture the volume in the first octant bounded by the planes $x + y + z = 6$, $2\,y = x$, $y = 2\,x$, $z = 3$, and the xy-plane.

5. Picture the volume in the first octant bounded by the planes $z = x + y$, $x + y = 4$, and the coördinate planes.

6. Picture the volume bounded by the planes $2\,z = x$, $y = x$, $x = 4$, $z = 0$, and $y = 0$.

7. Find the equation of the plane containing the z-axis and the point $(2, 3, 0)$.

8. Find the equation of the plane parallel to the x-axis whose intercepts on the y- and z-axes are 3 and 5, respectively.

9. Write the equation of the plane parallel to the y-axis whose trace in the xz-plane contains the points $(2, 0, 9)$ and $(6, 0, 1)$.

Write the equation of the plane determined by the following points:

10. $(5, 3, -1)$, $(3, -2, 3)$, $(2, 0, 2)$.
11. $(0, 0, 0)$, $(2, 6, 3)$, $(5, -7, 2)$.
12. $(2, 3, 5)$, $(4, -1, 3)$, $(3, -2, 1)$.
13. $(1, 1, 1)$, $(5, 1, 1)$, $(3, 2, 5)$.

14. Show that the equation of a plane whose x-, y-, and z-intercepts are a, b, and c, respectively, is $x/a + y/b + z/c = 1$.

15. Find the direction cosines of a line perpendicular to each of the following planes:

(a) $2x - y + 3z = 5$.   (c) $4x - 3y = 0$.

(b) $6x - 2y + 9z + 7 = 0$.   (d) $z = 2$.

16. Find the equation of the plane through $(3, 6, 2)$ perpendicular to the line joining that point to the origin.

17. Write the equation of the plane bisecting at right angles the line segment joining $(3, 6, -2)$ and $(5, -2, 4)$.

18. Write the equation of the plane through $(8, 3, 6)$ parallel to the plane $x - 3y + 2z = 1$.

19. If θ is the angle between the planes $a_1x + b_1y + c_1z + d_1 = 0$ and $a_2x + b_2y + c_2z + d_2 = 0$, show that

$$\cos \theta = \pm \frac{a_1a_2 + b_1b_2 + c_1c_2}{\sqrt{a_1^2 + b_1^2 + c_1^2} \cdot \sqrt{a_2^2 + b_2^2 + c_2^2}}.$$

(*Hint.* Consider the angle between two lines perpendicular to the planes, respectively.)

20. Show that the plane $2x + 2y + z + 5 = 0$ intersects the plane $5x + 4y - 3z - 2 = 0$ at an angle of $45°$.

21. Find the angle between the planes $2x + y - z + 8 = 0$ and $x + 2y + z - 4 = 0$.

22. Determine the angle which the plane $x + y + z - d = 0$ makes with each of the coördinate planes.

23. What is the condition that the planes in Exercise 19 be (a) perpendicular? (b) parallel? (c) coincident?

24. Show that the plane $9x - 6y + 2z - 11 = 0$ is parallel to the plane $18x - 12y + 4z - 55 = 0$. Find the distance between the two planes.

25. Show that the plane $3x - y + 2z = 6$ is perpendicular to the plane $6x + 4y - 7z + 2 = 0$.

26. Find the point of intersection of the following planes: $x + 2y + z - 6 = 0$, $3x - y - 2z + 5 = 0$, $4x + 3y - z + 1 = 0$.

27. Show analytically that the locus of points equidistant from $P_1(x_1, y_1, z_1)$ and $P_2(x_2, y_2, z_2)$ is a plane which bisects at right angles the line segment joining P_1 and P_2.

28. Find the point equidistant from $(0, 0, 0)$, $(2, 1, -5)$, $(1, 0, -3)$, and $(-1, 4, 1)$.

110. Equations of a straight line. A straight line is determined by the intersection of two planes. An indefinite number of planes pass through any straight line. The equations of any two of the planes through the line, considered as simultaneous equations, represent the line. It is usually convenient to represent a line by planes which are parallel to coördinate axes. The equations representing such planes have but two variables each.

111. Projecting planes. A plane parallel to the z-axis and passing through a given line is perpendicular to the xy-plane and cuts that plane in a line which is the projection of the given line upon the xy-plane. Similarly, planes through the given line and parallel to the y-axis and to the x-axis, respectively, cut the xz-plane and the yz-plane in lines which are the projections of the given line upon those planes. Such planes are called **projecting planes** of the line. Each line not parallel to an axis has three projecting planes and any two of them determine the line. The method of finding the projecting planes of a line whose equations are in the general form is illustrated in the following example.

EXAMPLE. Find the equations of the projecting planes of the line whose equations are

$$2x + 2y + 3z = 23$$
$$\text{and} \quad 4x + 3y + 9z = 52.$$

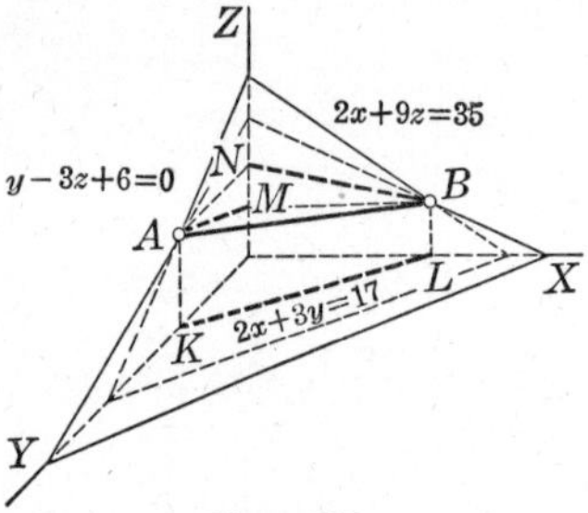

FIG. 113

Eliminating z, y, and x in turn from the given equations, we obtain

$$2x + 3y = 17, \ 2x + 9z = 35,$$
$$\text{and} \quad y - 3z + 6 = 0$$

as the three required equations. They represent the planes which project the given line upon the xy-, xz-, and yz-planes, respectively.

The segment AB in the figure represents a part of the given line, and AM, BN, and KL are segments of the traces of the three projecting planes in the coördinate planes.

112. Equations of a line through a point and in a given direction. Let (x_1, y_1, z_1) be the given point and let the direction cosines of the line be $\cos \alpha$, $\cos \beta$, and $\cos \gamma$. Let (x, y, z) be any other point on the line and call d the distance from (x_1, y_1, z_1) to (x, y, z). Then

$$d = \frac{x - x_1}{\cos \alpha} = \frac{y - y_1}{\cos \beta} = \frac{z - z_1}{\cos \gamma}.$$

These equalities exist for every d; hence the equations of the line through the point (x_1, y_1, z_1) and with direction cosines $\cos \alpha$, $\cos \beta$, and $\cos \gamma$ are

$$\frac{x - x_1}{\cos \alpha} = \frac{y - y_1}{\cos \beta} = \frac{z - z_1}{\cos \gamma}. \quad (5)$$

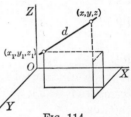

Fig. 114

Since equations (5) may be multiplied by the same constant without destroying the equality, it is not necessary that the denominators be the direction cosines of the line. It is sufficient that the denominators be proportional to the direction cosines. Thus the equations

$$\frac{x - x_1}{a} = \frac{y - y_1}{b} = \frac{z - z_1}{c} \quad (6)$$

are the equations of a line through the point (x_1, y_1, z_1) and with direction numbers a, b, and c. Equations (6) may be written in the form of equations (5) by dividing each denominator by $\pm \sqrt{a^2 + b^2 + c^2}$.

Equations (5) or (6) are frequently called the **symmetric** equations of a straight line. Either (5) or (6) are the equations of the projecting planes of the line.

EXAMPLE. Find the equations of the line through the point $(2, 1, -3)$ and parallel to the line through the points $(5, 2, 3)$ and $(0, 6, 2)$.

The direction cosines are proportional to the differences of corresponding coördinates, hence the direction cosines of the line through (5, 2, 3) and (0, 6, 2) are proportional to 5, $-$ 4, and 1. The required equations are, therefore,

$$\frac{x-2}{5} = \frac{y-1}{-4} = \frac{z+3}{1}.$$

113. Equations of a line through two given points. Let the given points be $P_1(x_1, y_1, z_1)$ and $P_2(x_2, y_2, z_2)$. The direction cosines are proportional to $x_2 - x_1$, $y_2 - y_1$, and $z_2 - z_1$. The equations of the line through P_1 and P_2 are, therefore, from equations (6) of the last section,

$$\frac{x-x_1}{x_2-x_1} = \frac{y-y_1}{y_2-y_1} = \frac{z-z_1}{z_2-z_1}.$$

114. Transformations of the general equations of a line to type forms. The following example will illustrate the method of transformation of the general equations of a line into type forms from which we can readily obtain certain properties of the line.

EXAMPLE. Transform the equations of the line

$$2x + 2y + 3z = 23 \quad \text{and} \quad 4x + 3y + 9z = 52,$$

in the example of Sec. 111, into type forms and find its direction cosines.

In that example we found the projecting planes of the given line to be

$$2x + 3y = 17, \quad 2x + 9z = 35, \quad \text{and} \quad y - 3z + 6 = 0. \quad (7)$$

Any two of these planes determine the line. Solving the first two equations of (7) for $2x$ (or for the common variable of any two of the equations), we may write

$$2x = -3y + 17 = -9z + 35.$$

Dividing by 18, and writing each variable with a positive sign, we have

$$\frac{x}{9} = \frac{y - \frac{17}{3}}{-6} = \frac{z - \frac{35}{9}}{-2}. \quad (8)$$

These are symmetric equations of a line through the point $(0, \frac{17}{3}, \frac{35}{9})$ and with direction numbers 9, $-$ 6, and $-$ 2.

We may obtain the symmetric equations of the line with direction cosines instead of direction numbers by dividing each denominator of equations (8) by 11. We thus obtain

$$\frac{x}{\frac{9}{11}} = \frac{y - \frac{17}{3}}{-\frac{6}{11}} = \frac{z - \frac{35}{9}}{-\frac{2}{11}}. \tag{9}$$

The direction cosines are $\cos \alpha = \frac{9}{11}$, $\cos \beta = -\frac{6}{11}$, and $\cos \gamma = -\frac{2}{11}$.

The same straight line is here represented in four different ways by the general equations in the example and by the type forms (7), (8), and (9).

EXERCISES

1. Find the projecting planes of the following lines and sketch each figure:

(a) $x + 2y + 2z = 10$ and $2x + y - z = 12$.
(b) $x + y + z = 15$ and $3y + 2z = 18$.
(c) $x + y = z$ and $x = 5$.
(d) $x + y = z$ and $y = x$.
(e) $\dfrac{x - 4}{2} = \dfrac{y - 1}{-2} = \dfrac{z - 3}{-1}$.

2. Find the points where each line of Exercise 1 pierces the coördinate planes.

3. Write the equations of each of the following lines:

(a) Through $(6, 2, 4)$ and with $\cos \alpha = \frac{8}{9}$, $\cos \beta = \frac{4}{9}$, $\cos \gamma = \frac{1}{9}$.
(b) Through $(-1, 3, -2)$ and with direction numbers $6, -3, 2$.
(c) Through $(0, -3, 8)$ and $(7, 2, 9)$.
(d) Through $(5, 2, 0)$ and parallel to the line joining the origin and $(8, 5, 1)$.
(e) Through $(3, 2, 0)$ and with $\cos \alpha = \frac{4}{5}$, $\cos \beta = \frac{3}{5}$.

4. Write the equations of the line through $(2, 6, 1)$ parallel to the line

$$\frac{x - 3}{11} = \frac{y - 1}{2} = \frac{z - 2}{10}.$$

5. Write the equations of the line through the origin making equal angles with the positive directions of the coördinate axes.

6. Show that the line determined by the points $(3, 1, 0)$ and $(1, 4, -3)$ is perpendicular to the line

$$\frac{x}{3} = \frac{y - 3}{8} = \frac{z + 7}{6}.$$

7. Show that the line

$$\frac{x-4}{-3} = \frac{y-1}{3} = \frac{z+1}{2}$$

lies in the plane $5x - y + 9z = 10$.

8. Write the equations of the line through $(5, 4, 8)$ and perpendicular to the plane $2x + 3y + 6z = 18$.

9. Find the foot of the perpendicular dropped from the point $(-8, 5, 2)$ upon the plane $3x - 2y - z + 8 = 0$.

10. Find the length of the perpendicular dropped from the point $(6, 0, -\frac{7}{2})$ upon the plane $8x + 6y - 5z = 3$.

11. Find the point on the line

$$\frac{x-5}{2} = \frac{y-11}{6} = \frac{z-12}{9}$$

equidistant from $(4, -1, 2)$ and $(-2, 3, 6)$.

12. Find symmetric equations of the line determined by the following planes:

(a) $x - 6y + 6z + 35 = 0$ and $2x - 2y - 3z = 0$.
(b) $2x - y - 2z = 13$ and $x - 2y + 2z + 7 = 0$.

13. Find the direction cosines of the line determined by the following planes:

(a) $4x - y - z = 12$ and $2x + y - 2z + 6 = 0$.
(b) $x - 2y - z + 2 = 0$ and $x - 5y - 5z + 4 = 0$.

14. Write symmetric equations of the line through the point $(-5, 2, -3)$ and parallel to the line determined by the planes $8x - 7y - 7z = 15$ and $4x - y - 6z = 20$.

MISCELLANEOUS EXERCISES

1. Find the equation of the plane parallel to the y-axis and containing the points $(7, 2, 1)$ and $(3, -4, 3)$.

2. Find the equation of the plane through $(-2, 1, 4)$ perpendicular to the line through $(8, 7, -1)$ and $(5, 2, 0)$.

3. Find the point equidistant from $(6, 0, 0)$, $(0, 6, 0)$, and $(0, 0, 12)$ and lying in the plane of these points.

4. Show that the planes $2x + y + z - 3 = 0$, $5x - y - 2 = 0$, $x + 2y + 2z - 3 = 0$, and $3x - 3y - 4z - 2 = 0$ meet in a common point.

5. Show that $(1, 4, 1)$, $(-3, 1, 0)$, $(5, 0, 1)$, and $(5, 7, 2)$ lie in a common plane.

6. Find the equation of the plane through $(1, 1, 1)$ and $(2, -2, -1)$ perpendicular to the plane $x + 3y - 8z + 2 = 0$.

7. Find the equation of the plane through $(1, -3, 2)$ perpendicular to the planes $x - 2y - 3z = 6$ and $3x + 4y - 4z = 1$.

8. Show that the distance from the plane whose equation is $x \cos \alpha + y \cos \beta + z \cos \gamma - p = 0$ to the point (x_1, y_1, z_1) is equal to $x_1 \cos \alpha + y_1 \cos \beta + z_1 \cos \gamma - p$. (See the method for finding the distance from a line to a point, Sec. 24.)

9. Find the distance from the plane $8x + 4y + z - 16 = 0$ to (a) $(5, 2, 4)$; (b) $(1, 1, 1)$; (c) $(3, -1, -4)$.

10. Show that the line

$$\frac{x - 2}{5} = \frac{y - 8}{-4} = \frac{z + 1}{9}$$

is parallel to the plane $6x + 3y - 2z - 3 = 0$, and find the distance from the plane to the line.

11. Find the distance from $(6, 1, 2)$ to the line

$$\frac{x - 2}{3} = \frac{y + 1}{-2} = \frac{z - 4}{4}.$$

12. Determine the angle which the line

$$\frac{x - 3}{1} = \frac{y + 1}{2} = \frac{z - 4}{-1}$$

makes with the plane $2x + y + z = 7$.

13. Find the equation of the plane containing the line

$$\frac{x + 3}{2} = \frac{y - 2}{-2} = \frac{z + 2}{3}$$

and the point $(1, -3, 6)$.

14. Show that the lines

$$\frac{x + 1}{3} = \frac{y - 6}{1} = \frac{z - 3}{2} \quad \text{and} \quad \frac{x - 6}{2} = \frac{y - 11}{2} = \frac{z - 3}{-1}$$

lie in a common plane, and find the equation of the plane.

15. Write the equations of the two lines through $(6, 4, 1)$ with $\cos \alpha = \frac{2}{3}$ and parallel to the plane $x + y - 4z - 12 = 0$.

CHAPTER X

SURFACES AND CURVES

115. Equation of a cylindrical surface with elements parallel to an axis. Let us consider an equation in two variables only, say in x and y,

$$x^2 + y^2 = 25. \tag{1}$$

In the xy-plane the equation represents a circle of radius 5 and with center at the origin. Let $P(x, y, 0)$ be a point on

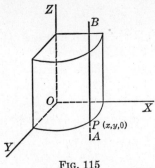

FIG. 115

the curve and draw through P a line AB parallel to the z-axis. The coördinates of any point on this line will satisfy equation (1) since each point on AB has the same x- and y-coördinates as P. Hence the coördinates of every point on the surface generated by moving P around the circle, keeping AB parallel to the z-axis, will satisfy equation (1). A surface which can be generated by moving a line parallel to a fixed position is called a **cylindrical surface.** Hence equation (1) represents a cylindrical surface with elements parallel to the z-axis and with any cross-section parallel to the xy-plane a circle of radius 5. The circle (1) is called a **directrix** of the cylindrical surface.

In a similar manner it can be shown that any equation in two variables represents a cylindrical surface with elements parallel to the axis corresponding to the variable which is lacking in the equation. Cylindrical surfaces are frequently given names corresponding to the directrix, such as elliptic, parabolic, etc. A plane may be looked upon as a cylindrical surface whose directrix is a straight line.

166

EXERCISES

Discuss the following cylindrical surfaces. Sketch each surface. In each case what curve will serve as a directrix?

1. $x^2 + z^2 = 16$.

2. $x^2 + y^2 - 2\,ax = 0$.

3. $y^2 + z^2 + 4\,y - 6\,z = 0$.

4. $2\,x - 3\,y = 6$.

5. $y^2 = 16\,x$.

6. $y^2 = 4 - x$.

7. $\dfrac{x^2}{16} + \dfrac{y^2}{9} = 1$.

8. $\dfrac{x^2}{a^2} + \dfrac{z^2}{b^2} = 1$.

9. $xz = 6$.

10. $y = x^3$.

11. $y^2 = x^3$.

12. $y^2 = x^4 - 4\,x^2$.

13. $y = \sin x$.

14. $y = \tan x$.

15. Find the equation of the locus of points equidistant from the yz-plane and the line determined by the planes $x = 4$ and $y = 0$. Interpret the result.

16. Find the locus of a point which moves so that the sum of its distances from the z-axis and the line $y = 0$, $x = 6$ is 10. Show that the locus is an elliptic cylindrical surface.

17. Rotate the x- and y-axes through $45°$, keeping the z-axis fixed, and show that $z^2 = 4 - x - y$ represents a cylindrical surface. What curve will serve as a directrix?

18. Rotate the x- and z-axes through $\tan^{-1} 2$ and show that $2\,z = 1 - x - y^2$ represents a cylindrical surface.

116. Surfaces of revolution. A surface formed by revolving a plane curve about some line in its plane has the property that cross-sections perpendicular to the axis of revolution are circles. The radius of the circle in each case is the distance from the axis to the point on the curve which is in the plane of the cross-section. This enables us to obtain the equation of the surface when we know the equation of the generating curve, as is illustrated in the following examples.

EXAMPLE 1. The circle in the xz-plane whose equation is $x^2 + z^2 = a^2$ is revolved about the z-axis. Find the equation of the spherical surface thus generated.

Any point P on the given circle will generate a circle with center at Q and with radius QP. The plane of QMP is paral-

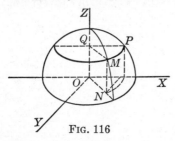

lel to the xy-plane. For any point M we have

$$x^2 + y^2 = \overline{ON}^2 = \overline{QM}^2 = \overline{QP}^2.$$

But QP is the x-coördinate of the point P in the xz-plane. From the given equation we have

$$QP = x = \sqrt{a^2 - z^2}.$$

Fig. 116

Hence the equation of the locus of P is

$$x^2 + y^2 = a^2 - z^2, \quad \text{or} \quad x^2 + y^2 + z^2 = a^2. \qquad (2)$$

But P is any point on the circle, hence equation (2) represents the spherical surface formed by revolving the circle about the z-axis.

EXAMPLE 2. The line in the xy-plane whose equation is $x + y = 6$ is revolved about the x-axis. Find the equation of the conical surface thus generated.

Any point P on the line generates a circle whose plane is parallel to the yz-plane. For any point M on this circle

$$y^2 + z^2 = \overline{QM}^2 = \overline{QP}^2.$$

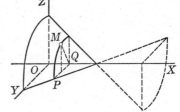

Fig. 117

But in the xy-plane $QP = y$, hence $QP = y = 6 - x$. The required equation of the conical surface is, therefore,

$$y^2 + z^2 = (6 - x)^2, \quad \text{or} \quad y^2 + z^2 - (6 - x)^2 = 0.$$

EXERCISES

1. Find the equation of each of the following surfaces generated as indicated, and sketch each surface:

(a) By revolving the parabola $z^2 = 4x$ about the x-axis.

(b) By revolving the ellipse $\dfrac{x^2}{25} + \dfrac{z^2}{9} = 1$ about the x-axis.

(c) By revolving the line $x + z = 4$ about the z-axis.

(d) By revolving the line $2\,x = 3\,y$ about the y-axis.

(e) By revolving the hyperbola $\dfrac{x^2}{a^2} - \dfrac{y^2}{b^2} = 1$ about (1) the x-axis; (2) the y-axis.

(f) By revolving the curve $y = \sin x$ about the x-axis.

2. Find the equation of the locus of points at a constant distance d from the point (x_1, y_1, z_1). Can this surface be interpreted as a surface of revolution? What is this locus?

3. Find the equation of the locus of points equidistant from the yz-plane and the point $(a, 0, 0)$. Interpret the result.

4. Find the equation of the locus of points such that the sum of their distances from $(0, 0, 15)$ and $(0, 0, -15)$ is equal to 34. Interpret the result.

Find a generating curve for each of the following surfaces of revolution:

5. $x^2 + z^2 = 2\,y.$

6. $x^2 + y^2 + z^2 = 16.$

7. $x^2 + y^2 + z^2 - 8\,x = 0.$

8. $x^2/16 + y^2/16 + z^2/9 = 1.$

9. $x^2 + y^2 = 6\,z.$

10. $4\,x^2 - y^2 + 4\,z^2 = 0.$

11. $x^2 + y^2 - (z - 3)^2 = 0.$

12. $z = e^{-(x^2 + y^2)}.$

13. Find the equation of the conical surface of revolution which cuts the xz-plane in the curve $x^2 + z^2 = 16$ and whose vertex is at $(0, 3, 0)$.

14. Find the equation of the surface formed by revolving the circle $x^2 + (z - b)^2 = a^2$ $(a < b)$ about the x-axis. (Such a surface is called a torus.)

117. Traces of a surface in the coördinate planes and in planes parallel to the coördinate planes. The curve in which a surface intersects a plane is called the **trace** of the surface in that plane. The trace of a surface in the xy-plane is found by intersecting the surface with the xy-plane, that is, by making $z = 0$ in the equation of the surface. Similarly, the xz- and yz-traces are found by making $y = 0$ and $x = 0$, respectively, in the equation of the surface. Thus the traces of the surface
$$4\,x^2 + y^2 - 2\,z = 8$$
in the xy-, yz-, and xz-planes, respectively, are
$$4\,x^2 + y^2 = 8, \quad y^2 - 2\,z = 8, \quad \text{and} \quad 4\,x^2 - 2\,z = 8.$$

The equation of any plane parallel to the xy-plane is of the form $z = k$. If we let $z = k$ in the equation of a surface, we have the equation of the trace of that surface in the plane $z = k$. Traces of a surface in planes parallel to the other coordinate planes are found in a similar manner.

118. Discussion of a surface. The discussion of a surface whose equation is given should include the following points:

(a) *Symmetry.* The same tests apply for symmetry with respect to the coördinate planes as those used in the plane for symmetry with respect to the axes.

(b) *Intercepts on the axes.*

(c) *Traces in the coördinate planes.*

(d) *Traces in planes parallel to each of the coördinate planes.* If all traces in planes parallel to a coördinate plane are circles, with centers on a line perpendicular to this coördinate plane, the surface is a surface of revolution. Find the generating curve.

(e) *Extent of the surface.*

Very little can be learned concerning a surface by locating points on the surface.

EXAMPLE 1. Discuss the locus of the equation

$$\frac{x^2}{a^2} + \frac{y^2}{b^2} + \frac{z^2}{c^2} = 1.$$

The surface is symmetric with respect to each of the coördinate planes. The intercepts are $\pm a$ on the x-axis, $\pm b$ on the y-axis, and $\pm c$ on the z-axis. The trace in the xy-plane is

$$\frac{x^2}{a^2} + \frac{y^2}{b^2} = 1.$$

This equation represents an ellipse with semiaxes a and b. Similarly, traces in the yz- and xz-planes are ellipses. Transposing z^2/c^2, we have

$$\frac{x^2}{a^2} + \frac{y^2}{b^2} = 1 - \frac{z^2}{c^2}.$$

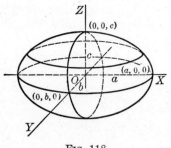

FIG. 118

Letting $z = \pm k$ $(k > 0)$ and dividing by $1 - k^2/c^2$, we obtain

$$\frac{x^2}{a^2\left(1 - \dfrac{k^2}{c^2}\right)} + \frac{y^2}{b^2\left(1 - \dfrac{k^2}{c^2}\right)} = 1.$$

The last equation shows that the sections of the surface by planes $z = \pm k$ are ellipses for $k < c$. The semiaxes $a\sqrt{1 - k^2/c^2}$ and $b\sqrt{1 - k^2/c^2}$ decrease as k approaches c in value. For $k = c$ the section is a point; and for $k > c$ the planes do not intersect the surface. Hence the surface lies between the planes $z = \pm c$, and each trace in a plane parallel to the xy-plane is an ellipse. Similarly, we can show that the surface lies between the planes $y = \pm b$ and between the planes $x = \pm a$, and that traces in planes parallel to the xz- and yz-planes, respectively, are ellipses. Such a surface is called an **ellipsoid**.

If $a = b$, traces in planes parallel to the xy-plane are circles and the surface is an ellipsoid of revolution. The generating curve is either the ellipse in the xz-plane,

$$\frac{x^2}{a^2} + \frac{z^2}{c^2} = 1,$$

or the ellipse in the yz-plane,

$$\frac{y^2}{b^2} + \frac{z^2}{c^2} = 1.$$

Similarly, if $b = c$ or if $a = c$, the surface is an ellipsoid of revolution.

If $a = b = c$, traces in planes parallel to the coördinate planes are circles and the surface is a sphere whose equation is
$$x^2 + y^2 + z^2 = a^2.$$

EXAMPLE 2. Discuss the locus of the equation

$$\frac{x^2}{a^2} + \frac{y^2}{b^2} - \frac{z^2}{c^2} = 1.$$

The surface is symmetric with respect to each of the coordinate planes. The intercepts are $\pm a$ on the x-axis and $\pm b$

on the y-axis. The surface does not cross the z-axis. The trace in the xy-plane is an ellipse and the traces in the yz- and the xz-planes are hyperbolas with transverse axes along the y- and the x-axes, respectively. Traces in planes $z = \pm k$

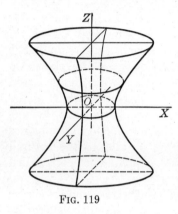

FIG. 119

are ellipses whose semiaxes, $a\sqrt{1 + k^2/c^2}$ and $b\sqrt{1 + k^2/c^2}$, increase as k increases. Traces in the planes $y = \pm h$ are hyperbolas,

$$\frac{x^2}{a^2} - \frac{z^2}{c^2} = 1 - \frac{h^2}{b^2},$$

with transverse axes in the xy-plane for values of h less than b. Traces in the planes $y = \pm h = \pm b$ are the straight lines

$$\frac{x}{a} \pm \frac{z}{c} = 0.$$

For values of h greater than b the traces are hyperbolas with transverse axes in the yz-plane. Similarly, traces in planes parallel to the yz-plane are hyperbolas or straight lines. Such a surface is called a **hyperboloid of one sheet**.

EXAMPLE 3. Discuss the locus of the equation

$$\frac{x^2}{a^2} - \frac{y^2}{b^2} - \frac{z^2}{c^2} = 1.$$

The surface is symmetric with respect to each of the coördinate planes. The intercepts are $\pm a$ on the x-axis. The surface does not intersect the other axes. Traces in planes $x = \pm k$ parallel to the yz-plane are given by the equation

$$\frac{y^2}{b^2} + \frac{z^2}{c^2} = \frac{k^2}{a^2} - 1.$$

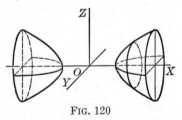

FIG. 120

This equation shows that for $k < a$ the planes do not inter-

sect the surface and hence the surface is outside the two
planes $x = \pm a$. For $k > a$ the sections are ellipses whose
semiaxes increase as k increases. Traces in planes parallel
to the xy- and xz-planes, respectively, are hyperbolas. This
surface is called an **elliptic hyperboloid of two sheets.** In case
$b = c$, the surface is a surface of
revolution.

EXAMPLE 4. Discuss the locus
of the equation

$$\frac{x^2}{a^2} + \frac{y^2}{b^2} = cz.$$

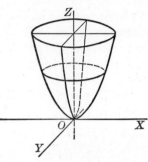

The surface is symmetric with
respect to the xz- and yz-planes.
It touches the xy-plane at the
origin but does not extend below
that plane if c is positive, nor
above that plane if c is negative.

FIG. 121

The traces in the xz- and yz-planes are the parabolas
$x^2 = a^2cz$ and $y^2 = b^2cz$, respectively. Traces in planes parallel to the xy-plane are ellipses with increasing semiaxes as
the intersecting plane is moved farther and farther from
the xy-plane. The surface is called an **elliptic paraboloid** if
$a \neq b$, and a paraboloid of revolution if $a = b$. The figure is
drawn for c positive.

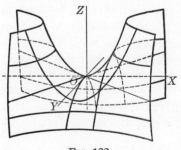

FIG. 122

EXAMPLE 5. Discuss the
locus of the equation

$$\frac{x^2}{a^2} - \frac{y^2}{b^2} = cz.$$

The surface is symmetric
with respect to the xz- and
yz-planes. The origin is on
the surface and the axes intersect the surface in no other
point. The traces in the xy-, the yz-, and the xz-planes,
respectively, are the lines $x/a \pm y/b = 0$, the parabola

$y^2 = -b^2cz$, and the parabola $x^2 = a^2cz$. Traces of the surface in planes parallel to the xy-plane are hyperbolas with the transverse axes in the xz-plane when the intersecting planes are above the xy-plane and with the transverse axes in the yz-plane when the intersecting planes are below the xy-plane. For c positive, as in Fig. 122, traces of the surface in planes parallel to the xz-plane are found to be parabolas, concave upward, with vertices on the parabola which is the trace of the surface in the yz-plane. Similarly, the traces in planes parallel to the yz-plane are found to be parabolas, concave downward, with vertices on the parabola which is the trace of the surface in the xz-plane. This surface is called a **hyperbolic paraboloid.**

EXAMPLE 6.   Discuss the locus of the equation

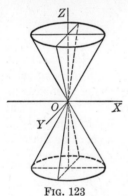

FIG. 123

$$\frac{x^2}{a^2} + \frac{y^2}{b^2} - \frac{z^2}{c^2} = 0.$$

The surface is symmetric with respect to each of the three coördinate planes. The origin is on the surface and there are no other intercepts on the axes. The trace in the xy-plane is a point; the trace in the xz-plane is the lines $x/a \pm z/c = 0$; and the trace in the yz-plane is the lines $y/b \pm z/c = 0$. Traces in planes parallel to the xy-plane are ellipses with increasing semiaxes as the intersecting plane is moved farther and farther from the xy-plane. Traces of the surface in planes parallel to the xz- and the yz-planes are hyperbolas with transverse axes parallel to the z-axis. The surface is an **elliptic cone** with axis along the z-axis. In case $a = b$, the surface is a right circular cone.

The foregoing examples are illustrations of a class of surfaces called **quadric** surfaces. They are represented by equations of the second degree and have the property that a section cut by any plane is a conic.

EXERCISES

Discuss the surfaces represented by the following equations:

1. $\dfrac{x^2}{25} + \dfrac{y^2}{16} + \dfrac{z^2}{9} = 1.$

4. $\dfrac{x^2}{25} - \dfrac{y^2}{16} + \dfrac{z^2}{9} = 0.$

2. $\dfrac{x^2}{25} - \dfrac{y^2}{16} + \dfrac{z^2}{9} = 1.$

5. $\dfrac{x^2}{25} - \dfrac{y^2}{16} + \dfrac{z^2}{9} = -1.$

3. $\dfrac{x^2}{25} - \dfrac{y^2}{16} - \dfrac{z^2}{9} = 1.$

6. $\dfrac{x^2}{25} - \dfrac{y^2}{16} - \dfrac{z^2}{9} = 0.$

Discuss the surfaces represented by the following equations:

7. $x^2 + y^2 + z^2 = 20.$

11. $x^2 + y^2 + z^2 - 2\,ax = 0.$

8. $9\,x^2 + 4\,y^2 + z^2 = 36.$

12. $(x - 2)^2 = 4\,y^2 + z^2.$

9. $y^2 + 2\,z^2 = 8\,x.$

13. $\dfrac{x^2}{9} - \dfrac{y^2}{16} = 2\,z.$

10. $4\,x^2 - 9\,y^2 = 0.$

14. $4\,z = 36 - x^2 - y^2.$

15. $\dfrac{(x - 2)^2}{9} + \dfrac{(y - 3)^2}{25} + \dfrac{(z - 1)^2}{16} = 1.$

16. $x^2 + y^2 + z = 4.$

17. $x^2 + y^2 + z^2 - 12\,x - 6\,y - 4\,z = 0.$

18. $25\,x^2 + 25\,y^2 - 16(z - 3)^2 = 400.$

19. $(x - 1)^2 + 4(y - 2)^2 = 9(z - 2)^2.$

20. $y^2 + 2\,z^2 + 16 = 8\,x.$

21. Show that $x^2 - y^2 = az$ becomes $2\,x'y' = az$ by rotating the x- and y-axes through an angle of $-45°$, keeping the z-axis fixed.

Discuss the surfaces represented by the following equations:

22. $2\,z = 1 - x - y^2.$

23. $(x + y)^2 + z^2 = 9.$

119. The locus of an equation in three variables. The elimination of z between the equations $f(x, y, z) = 0$ and $z = c$ results in the equation

$$f(x, y, c) = 0.$$

This equation represents a cylindrical surface with elements parallel to the z-axis. This surface cuts the xy-plane in a curve which is congruent to the curve cut from the plane $z = c$ by the same surface. Hence we may look upon $f(x, y, c) = 0$

as the equation of a cylindrical surface or as the equation of
the curve in which that cylindrical surface cuts the xy-plane.
But the equation $f(x, y, c) = 0$ is satisfied by all the points
whose coördinates satisfy the equations $f(x, y, z) = 0$ and $z = c$
simultaneously. Hence the plane $z = c$ intersects the locus
represented by $f(x, y, z) = 0$ in a plane curve which is congruent to the curve in the xy-plane represented by $f(x, y, c) = 0$.
It was pointed out in Sec. 38 that an equation in two variables, such as $f(x, y, c) = 0$, represents in a plane either a curve,
isolated points, or no real locus. Hence the plane $z = c$ may
intersect the locus of $f(x, y, z) = 0$ in a plane curve, in isolated
points, or in no real locus. A similar statement holds for
planes parallel to the other coördinate planes. Hence the locus
represented by an equation in three variables, $f(x, y, z) = 0$,
is a surface, isolated points or lines, or no real locus.

120. Intersection of surfaces. Curves. Two surfaces will,
in general, intersect in a curve. The equations of two surfaces, therefore, considered simultaneously represent the
curve of intersection of the two surfaces. From the equations of two surfaces,

$$f_1(x, y, z) = 0 \quad \text{and} \quad f_2(x, y, z) = 0, \tag{3}$$

we obtain by eliminating one of the variables, say z, one
equation in two variables,

$$\phi(x, y) = 0. \tag{4}$$

Equation (4) represents a cylindrical surface with elements
parallel to the z-axis and is satisfied by all the points whose
coördinates satisfy equations (3) simultaneously. Equation (4) represents, therefore, a cylindrical surface through
the curve of intersection of the surfaces represented by equations (3). This surface intersects the xy-plane in a curve
whose equation is $\quad \phi(x, y) = 0.$

This curve is the projection upon the xy-plane of the curve of
intersection of the surfaces represented by equations (3).
Similarly, the elimination of y and of x, respectively, from
equations (3) will give the cylindrical surfaces which project

the curve of intersection of the surfaces upon the xz- and the yz-planes.

In general, the curve of intersection of two surfaces is not a plane curve. A curve which does not lie in a plane is called a **skew** curve.

EXAMPLE 1. Find the equations of the projections upon the coördinate planes of the curve of intersection of the ellipsoid $x^2 + 2\,y^2 + 9\,z^2 = 36$ and the plane $y = 2\,x$.

Eliminating x, y, and z in turn, we obtain

$$y^2 + 4\,z^2 = 16,$$
$$x^2 + z^2 = 4,$$

and
$$y = 2\,x$$

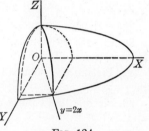

as the equations of the projections of the curve of intersection of the two surfaces upon the yz-, the xz-, and the xy-planes, respectively.

FIG. 124

EXERCISES

Find the equations of the projections upon the coördinate planes of the curves of intersection of the surfaces whose equations are given, and make a sketch in each case:

1. $x^2 + y^2 = 16$ and $x = 3$.
2. $x^2 + y^2 = 16$ and $z = 4$.
3. $x^2 + y^2 = 16$ and $x + z = 5$.
4. $x^2 + y^2 = 16$ and $x + y + z = 8$.
5. $x^2 + y^2 + z^2 = 64$ and $y = 4$.
6. $x^2 + y^2 + z^2 = 64$ and $y = \sqrt{3}\,x$.
7. $x^2 + y^2 + z^2 = 64$ and $2\,x + 2\,y + z = 18$.
8. $x^2 + y^2 + z^2 = 64$ and $y^2 + z^2 = 48$.
9. $y^2 = 4\,x$ and $x = 2$.
10. $y^2 = 4\,x$ and $z = 2$.
11. $y^2 = 4 - x$ and $z = x$.
12. $y = x^2$ and $x^2 + z^2 = 1$.

13. $x^2 + y^2 = 2\ ax$ and $x^2 + y^2 = az$.

14. $y^2 + z^2 = 2\ x$ and $x - y = 4$.

15. $x^2 = y^2 + 3\ z^2$ and $2\ x + y = 4$.

16. $x^2 = y^2 + 3\ z^2$ and $x + y = 3$.

17. $x^2 + y^2 + z^2 = 16$ and $x^2 + y^2 - 4\ x = 0$.

18. $x^2 + y^2 + z^2 = 16$ and $z = x + y$.

19. $x^2 + y^2 + z^2 = 16$ and $y^2 = 6\ x$.

20. $x^2 + y^2 + z^2 - 8\ x = 0$ and $x = z$.

21. $z = 1 - x^2$ and $x = 1 - y^2$.

22. $2\ z = 4 - x^2 - y^2$ and $y + z = 2$.

23. $x^2 + y^2 = 2\ z$ and $2\ x^2 - 2\ y^2 - z^2 = 0$.

24. Picture the volume in the first octant bounded by the surfaces $x^2 = 4\ y$, $y^2 = 4\ x$, and $z = 4$.

25. Picture the volume in the first octant bounded by the surface $x = 4 - z - y^2$ and lying under the plane $y + z = 2$.

26. Picture the volume bounded by the surfaces $y^2 + z^2 = 4$ and $x^2 + z^2 = 4$.

27. Picture the volume in the first octant bounded by the surfaces $4\ y^2 + 4\ z^2 = x^2$, $x = 4\ y$, $x = 8$, and $z = 0$.

28. A right circular cylinder with altitude equal to the diameter of the base is cut by a plane which cuts one base in a diameter and is tangent to the other base. Picture the smaller of the two parts into which the cylinder is divided. Select axes and write the equations of the surfaces which bound the part pictured.

121. Spherical coördinates. Another method of locating a point in space is by giving its distance and direction from a fixed point. In Fig. 125 let O be the fixed point and draw OX and OZ making $\angle XOZ = 90°$.

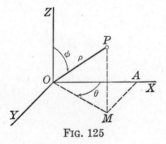

FIG. 125

Let θ be the angle between the plane POZ and the plane XOZ and let ϕ be the angle between the lines OP and OZ. The point P is determined by ρ, θ, and ϕ.

If OX and OZ are chosen for the x- and z-axes, respectively, and OY is drawn perpendicular to OX and OZ, relations between the spherical and rectangular coördinates of P are easily found. Draw PM perpendicular to the plane XOY and join O and M. Then $\angle MOP = 90° - \phi$, and $OM = OP \cos \angle MOP = \rho \cos(90° - \phi) = \rho \sin \phi$. Hence the rectangular coördinates are

$$x = OA = OM \cos \theta = \rho \sin \phi \cos \theta,$$
$$y = AM = OM \sin \theta = \rho \sin \phi \sin \theta,$$
$$z = MP = \rho \cos \phi.$$

The spherical coördinates can be expressed in terms of the rectangular coördinates by solving the foregoing equations for ρ, ϕ, and θ. Squaring and adding, we have

$$x^2 + y^2 + z^2 = \rho^2, \quad \text{or} \quad \rho = \pm\sqrt{x^2 + y^2 + z^2}.$$

Then from the third of the foregoing equations we obtain

$$\phi = \cos^{-1} \frac{z}{\sqrt{x^2 + y^2 + z^2}},$$

and from the first and second equations we obtain

$$\theta = \tan^{-1}\frac{y}{x}.$$

122. Cylindrical coördinates. Cylindrical coördinates are a combination of polar and rectangular coördinates. Thus in Fig. 126 the cylindrical coördinates of P are (r, θ, z), where r and θ are the polar coördinates of M, the projection of P upon the xy-plane, and where z is the distance MP.

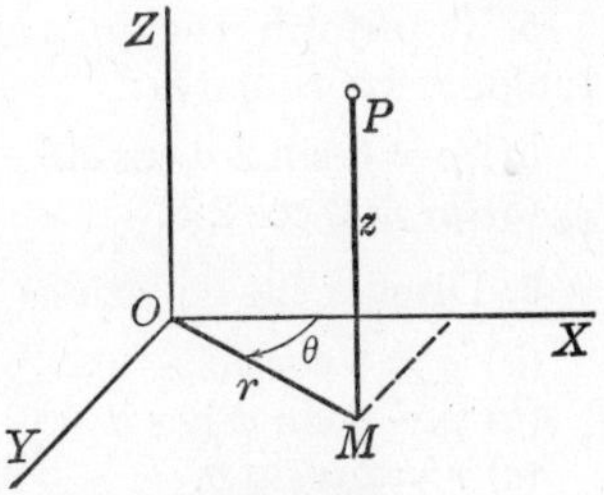

The rectangular coördinates (x, y, z) of P are related to the cylindrical coördinates (r, θ, z) of P by the equations

Fig. 126

$$x = r \cos \theta, \quad y = r \sin \theta, \quad z = z.$$

The cylindrical coördinates (r, θ, z) of P are related to the spherical coördinates (ρ, θ, ϕ) of P by the equations

$$r = \rho \sin \phi, \quad \theta = \theta, \quad z = \rho \cos \phi.$$

EXERCISES

1. Write the rectangular and the cylindrical coördinates of the points whose spherical coördinates are

$(a)\ \left(8, \dfrac{\pi}{4}, \dfrac{\pi}{3}\right).$ $(c)\ \left(2, 0, \dfrac{\pi}{4}\right).$

$(b)\ \left(8, \dfrac{\pi}{4}, \dfrac{2\,\pi}{3}\right).$ $(d)\ \left(3, \dfrac{\pi}{2}, \dfrac{\pi}{2}\right).$

2. Write the rectangular and the spherical coördinates of the points whose cylindrical coördinates are

$(a)\ \left(5, \dfrac{\pi}{6}, 6\right).$ $(c)\ \left(4, \dfrac{\pi}{3}, -2\right).$

$(b)\ \left(-5, -\dfrac{\pi}{6}, 6\right).$ $(d)\ (4, 0, 0).$

3. Write the spherical and the cylindrical coördinates of the points whose rectangular coördinates are

$(a)\ (6, 3, 0).$ $(c)\ (0, 4, 2).$

$(b)\ (-5, 0, 0).$ $(d)\ (4\sqrt{3}, 4, 8).$

4. Transform the following equations into equations in cylindrical or spherical coördinates. Choose the form which gives the simpler equation.

$(a)\ x^2 + y^2 = 5\,z.$

$(b)\ xz = ay.$

$(c)\ x^2 + z^2 = 3\,y.$

$(d)\ (x^2 + y^2 + z^2)^2 = 3\,axyz.$

5. Transform the following equations into equations in rectangular coördinates:

$(a)\ \rho = 3 \sin 2\,\theta \cos \phi.$

$(b)\ \rho^2 = 2 \cos 2\,\theta.$

$(c)\ z = a - r.$

$(d)\ r^2 + a^2z^2 = b^2.$

6. Discuss the equations

$(a)\ \rho = 8 \cos \phi.$

$(b)\ \rho - 6 \sin \phi \cos \theta = 0.$

$(c)\ r = 2\,a \sin \theta.$

$(d)\ a^2r^2 - b^2z^2 = c^2.$

$(e)\ b^2z^2 - a^2r^2 = c^2.$

$(f)\ \rho = a \csc 2\,\theta \cot \phi \csc \phi.$

7. A circular cylinder of diameter 6 inches intersects a sphere of radius 6 inches so that an element of the cylinder coincides with a diameter of the sphere. Choose axes and write the equations of the bounding surfaces of the common volume in (a) rectangular coördinates; (b) spherical coördinates; (c) cylindrical coördinates.

MISCELLANEOUS EXERCISES

1. What surfaces are represented by the following equations?

(a) $x^2 + z^2 = a^2$.

(b) $x^2 = 2\,py$.

(c) $y = mx + b$.

(d) $y^2 - z^2 = 0$.

(e) $xyz = 0$.

(f) $x^2 + y^2 = z^2$.

(g) $x^2 + 2\,y^2 + 3\,z^2 = 4$.

(h) $xy = z^2$.

(i) $x + y = z^2$.

(j) $x^2 + y^2 = z$.

2. Find the equation of the right circular cylinder whose axis is the line $x = 3$, $y = 4$ and whose radius is 5.

3. Find the equation of the sphere which passes through $(0, 0, 0)$, $(1, 3, 2)$, $(1, 2, -3)$, and $(5, 3, 6)$.

4. Show that the plane $5\,x - y - 4\,z + 31 = 0$ is tangent to the sphere $x^2 + y^2 + z^2 - 8\,x - 2\,y - 4\,z = 21$, and write the equation of the parallel tangent plane.

5. Find the points where the line $x - 2\,y - 2\,z + 6 = 0$, $x + 2\,z - 2 = 0$ intersects the cone $4\,x^2 + 4\,z^2 - y^2 = 0$.

6. Find the equation of the surface of revolution generated by revolving the hyperbola $xy = a^2$ about one of its asymptotes.

7. The arc of the parabola $x^{\frac{1}{2}} + y^{\frac{1}{2}} = a^{\frac{1}{2}}$ from $(a, 0)$ to $(0, a)$ in the xy-plane is revolved about the x-axis. Find the equation of the surface thus generated.

8. The four-cusped hypocycloid $x^{\frac{2}{3}} + y^{\frac{2}{3}} = a^{\frac{2}{3}}$ is revolved about the x-axis. Find the equation of the surface thus generated.

9. The line $x + z = 2$ is revolved about the line $z = 2$ in the xz-plane. Find the equation of the surface thus generated.

10. Find the equation of the surface of revolution generated by revolving the arc of the parabola $y^2 = 4\,px$ terminated by the ends of the latus rectum about the latus rectum.

11. Discuss the surface $x^{\frac{2}{3}} + y^{\frac{2}{3}} + z^{\frac{2}{3}} = a^{\frac{2}{3}}$.

12. Show that in general the parametric equations $x = f_1(t)$, $y = f_2(t)$, $z = f_3(t)$ represent a skew curve.

13. Discuss the curve $x = t$, $y = t^2$, $z = t^3$.

14. Discuss the curve $x = a \cos t$, $y = a \sin t$, $z = kt$. (This curve is called a helix.)

ANSWERS

(The answers to some of the exercises are omitted in order to give the student experience in checking his own work. Teachers who desire answers to the other exercises should communicate with the publishers.)

Page 7

9. (a) 10. (b) -12. (c) 15. (d) -6. **11.** 99.

10. (a) 16. (b) 56. (c) 35. (d) 29. (e) $\dfrac{a^2 - b^2}{2}$. **12.** 69.

Pages 9–10

1. (a) 10. (b) 13. (c) $2\sqrt{13}$. (d) $3\sqrt{10}$. (e) $3\sqrt{5}$. (f) $5\sqrt{2}$.

2. 36. **8.** $(\frac{3}{2}, 0)$. **10.** $(-2, 2)$.

6. $5\sqrt{5}, 5\sqrt{5}$. **9.** $(0, -2)$. **11.** $(1, 0)$.

12. $(5, 5)$. **13.** $\left(4 + 3\sqrt{3}, 3 - 4\sqrt{3}\right)$ or $\left(4 - 3\sqrt{3}, 3 + 4\sqrt{3}\right)$.

14. $(\frac{7}{5}, \frac{24}{5})$, $(\frac{7}{5}, -\frac{24}{5})$, $(-\frac{7}{5}, \frac{24}{5})$, $(-\frac{7}{5}, -\frac{24}{5})$.

Pages 11–12

2. $(1, 4), (0, -2), (4, 2)$. **9.** $(7.2, 4.8)$.

3. $(-2, -\frac{5}{4}), (2, \frac{1}{2}), (6, \frac{9}{4})$. **10.** $12, 3\sqrt{5}, 3\sqrt{13}$.

5. 40. **11.** $(3, 2)$.

6. (a) $(2,3)$. (b) $(-34,-9)$. (c) $(41,16)$. **13.** $(7, 9), (-5, 1), (3, -3)$.

7. $(5, 3), (10, 5\frac{1}{2})$. **14.** $(-2, 1), (10, -3)$.

8. $\left(1 + 3\sqrt{10}, 3 + \sqrt{10}\right)$. **15.** $(7, 1), (1, -7)$.

Pages 15–16

1. (a) 1. (b) 2. (c) $-\frac{2}{3}$. (d) 0. **11.** $\frac{1}{5}, -5$.

4. $\frac{9}{11}, 9, 0$. **12.** $2, -\frac{1}{2}$.

7. $45°$. **13.** $-2 - \sqrt{3}, -2 + \sqrt{3}, 1$.

8. (a) $80° 50'$. (b) $67° 23'$. **14.** $\tan^{-1}\left(\pm \dfrac{m^2 - 1}{2\,m}\right)$.

9. (a) $45°, 63° 26', 71° 34'$. (b) $26° 34', 49° 24', 104° 2'$. (c) $33° 41'$, $56° 19', 90°$. (d) $26° 34', 18° 26', 135°$. (e) $45°, 63° 26', 71° 34'$.

Pages 23–24

2. (a) 5, 5. (c) $-\frac{2}{5}$, $-\frac{2}{3}$.

5. (a) $2x - y = 8$. (b) $3x + 2y = 5$. (c) $2x + 3y = 0$. (d) $y + 2 = 0$.
(e) $x = 3$. (f) $x - y = 5$.

6. $3x - 4y + 15 = 0$, $4x + 3y = 5$.

7. (a) $x - y = 0$. (b) $x + y = 0$.

9. $x = 0$, $x = 8$, $y = 0$, $y = 4$, $x - 2y = 0$, $x + 2y = 8$.

10. $y = 5$, $x - y = 0$, $x + y = 0$.

11. $x - y = 0$, $5x + y = 16$, $x + 5y = 16$.

12. $7x - 3y + 10 = 0$, $5x + y = 18$, $x - 2y = 8$.

13. $x = 0$, $y = x$, $x + y = 12$.

14. $y = 0$, $y = \sqrt{3}\,x$, $y + \sqrt{3}\,x = a\sqrt{3}$.

15. $x - 3y = 0$.

18. $x + 4y = 1$, $4x - y = 4$.

19. $2x + 18y = 41$, $18x + 2y = 49$.

20. $3x - 5y + 14 = 0$, $3x - 5y = 20$,
$5x + 3y + 12 = 0$, $5x + 3y = 22$.

Pages 26–27

1. (a) $y = -\frac{3}{4}x + 3$, $m = -\frac{3}{4}$, $b = 3$.

2. (a) $\frac{1}{4}x + \frac{1}{3}y = 1$.

5. (a) 45°. (b) 60°.

6. 45°, 135°.

7. (a) $(0, -1)$, $(5, 0)$, $(\frac{1}{2}, 3)$, and
$(-\frac{3}{2}, 2)$. (b) $(5\frac{1}{2}, -3)$, $(7\frac{1}{2}, 2)$,
$(0, 5)$, and $(-2, 0)$.

8. $3x + 7y = 47$, $7x - 3y = 13$.

9. (a) 5. (b) $2\sqrt{10}$.

10. $(9, 7)$.

11. $3\sqrt{10}$, $6\sqrt{2}$.

12. $(-1, -7)$.

13. $(3, 0)$, $(-5, -4)$.

Pages 32–34

1. (a) $\dfrac{\sqrt{2}\,x}{2} + \dfrac{\sqrt{2}\,y}{2} - 2 = 0$. (c) $-x - 5 = 0$. (e) $\dfrac{\sqrt{3}\,x}{2} + \frac{1}{2}y = 0$.

2. (a) $\frac{3}{5}x + \frac{4}{5}y - 2 = 0$, $\omega = 53°\,8'$, $p = 2$.

(c) $-\dfrac{\sqrt{2}\,x}{2} - \dfrac{\sqrt{2}\,y}{2} - 4\sqrt{2} = 0$, $\omega = \dfrac{5\,\pi}{4}$, $p = 4\sqrt{2}$.

5. $\pm\dfrac{b}{\sqrt{1 + m^2}}$.

6. (a) 2. (b) -3. (c) 0. (d) -2.6.

8. 5.

9. (a) $\dfrac{3\sqrt{2}}{2}$. (b) $-\dfrac{\sqrt{2}}{2}$.

11. (a) $\sqrt{5}$. (b) $3\sqrt{10}$.

12. 20 square units.

13. (a) $4x + 2y = 25$. (b) $x - 3y + 5 = 0$.

14. $12x + 5y = 0$, $12x + 5y = 78$.

15. $(3, 6)$, $(-1, -2)$.

16. 8, $4\sqrt{5}$, 8.

17. 15 square units.

18. $4x - 4y + 9 = 0$, $8x + 8y = 15$.

19. $7x + y = 3$, $x + 13y + 6 = 0$, $12x - 14y = 13$.

20. 2.5.

Pages 36–37

2. $3x + 8y = c$, $3x + 8y = 20$; $8x - 3y = c$, $8x - 3y = 29$.

3. (a) $y = -x + 5$. (b) $y = -x + 5$. (c) $y = \pm \frac{3}{4}x + 5$. (d) $y = 5$.
(e) Impossible.

4. $5x - 2y = c$, $5x - 2y = 12$. **5.** $x + 2y = c$, $x + 2y = 11$.

6. (a) $x + 3y = 4$, $x - \frac{1}{3}y = 4$. (b) $x + \frac{1}{2}y = 4$.

7. $x \cos \omega + y \sin \omega - 5 = 0$, $\frac{4}{5}x + \frac{3}{5}y - 5 = 0$.

8. $\frac{3}{5}x - \frac{4}{5}y - 5 = 0$, $-\frac{3}{5}x + \frac{4}{5}y - 5 = 0$.

9. $3x + 2y = 12$, $x + y = 5$. **10.** $x + 5y = 10$.

11. (a) $x + 2y = 10$, $8x + y = 20$. (b) $2x + y = 8$. (c) Impossible.

Pages 38–39

1. (a) $x - 4y + 23 = 0$. (b) $5x + 3y = 0$, $x + 3y = 12$. (c) $x + 3 = 0$,
$8x + 15y = 51$.

2. $5x + 3y = 0$. **3.** $5x - y - 3 = 0$. **4.** $11x + 22y + 6 = 0$.

5. (a) $x - y = 2$. (b) $x - y = 2$. (c) $x - y = 2$, $17x - 7y = 26$.

6. $3x + 2y = 18$, $6x + y = 18$.

7. (a) $3x + 4y = 10$, $x = 2$. (b) $2x + y = 5$. (c) Impossible.

Pages 39–41. Miscellaneous Exercises

1. $a = -\frac{25}{11}$, $b = \frac{25}{2}$, $m = \frac{11}{2}$, $p = \sqrt{5}$, $\omega = 169° 42'$.

2. $a = \frac{5}{3}$, $b = \frac{5}{2}$. **5.** $(2, -1)$.

3. $(2, 6)$. **6.** $a = 4$.

4. $(10, 3)$. **7.** $c = -9$.

9. $x + y = a$, $y = (2 + \sqrt{3})(x - a)$, $y = (2 - \sqrt{3})x + a$.

10. 6.

11. $x + 2y + 6 = 0$, $3x + y = 17$; $x + y = 1$, $x - 3y = 9$.

12. $(4, 2)$, $(0, -3)$, $(-8, -6)$, $(-4, -1)$.

13. $8x - y = 6$, $16x - 2y = 61$, $x + 8y + 23 = 0$, $x + 8y + 9 = 0$.

14. $8\sqrt{5}$. **17.** $x - y + 5 = 0$, $7x - y = 7$.

15. $4\sqrt{10}$. **18.** $x - 2y = 3$.

16. $y = 6$, $3x + 4y = 30$. **19.** 220 feet.

Pages 54–55

1. $(\frac{2}{3}, -2)$, $(6, 6)$. **17.** $(\pm 2\sqrt{2}, 2)$.

3. $(0, 0)$, $(4, 8)$, $(-4, -8)$. **19.** $(3, \frac{3}{2})$, $(3, \frac{3}{2})$, $(0, 3)$.

4. $(3, 5)$, $(3, 5)$. **21.** $(-1, 1)$, $(-1, 1)$, $(\frac{1}{2}, 4)$.

5. No intersections. **23.** $(0, 0)$, $(0, 0)$, $(\frac{1}{2}, \frac{1}{8})$.

7. $(2, 4)$, $(-2, -4)$, $(4, 2)$, $(-4, -2)$. **25.** $(2, 3)$, $(2, 3)$, $(0, -1)$.

9. $(2, \pm 8)$, $(-2, \pm 8)$. **27.** $(0, 0)$, $(1, 1)$, $(4, 4)$.

11. $(1, -2)$, $(4, 4)$. **29.** $c = \pm 10$.

13. $(-3, 0)$, $(2, \pm \sqrt{5})$. **30.** $b = 1$.

15. $(1, -1)$. **31.** $m = -\frac{1}{4}b^2$.

Pages 57–59

1. $x = 3$, $y = \pm 2$.
2. (a) $x^2 + y^2 = 25$.
   (b) $(x - 1)^2 + (y - 2)^2 = 16$.
4. (a) $y = 2\,x^2$.
   (b) $2\,x = 1$, $y = 0$.
5. $x^2(x^2 + y^2) = y^2$.
6. $4\,x - 3\,y = 16$.
7. $x^2 + y^2 - 4\,x - 3\,y = 0$.
10. $x^2 - y^2 = 0$.
11. $y^2 = 6\,x - 9$.
12. $y^2 + 12\,x = 0$.

13. $x^2 - 8\,x = 8\,y$.
14. (a) $3\,x^2 + 4\,y^2 = 48$.
    (b) $3\,x^2 + 4\,y^2 = 48$.
15. $3\,x^2 + 4\,y^2 = 48$.
16. $3\,x^2 - y^2 = 48$.
17. $9\,x^2 - 16\,y^2 = 144$.
18. $x^2 + y^2 + 2\,x = 8$.
19. $3\,x^2 - 2\,xy + 3\,y^2 = 8$.
20. $x^2 + 2\,xy + y^2 + 8\sqrt{2}\,x - 8\sqrt{2}\,y = 0$.
21. $xy - 3\,x + 2\,y = 0$.
22. $y = 0$, $xy = x^2 - 1$.

Pages 62–63

1. $x'^2 + y'^2 = 36$.
2. $x'^2 + 2\,y'^2 = 16$.
3. $y'^2 = 2\,x'$.
4. $4\,x'^2 + 4\,y'^2 = 129$.
5. $3\,x'^2 - y'^2 = 27$.
6. $x'^2 + 4\,y' = 4$.
7. $x'^2 = 2\,y'$.

8. $x' + 2\,y' = 0$, $3\,x' - 7\,y' = 0$.
9. $Ax' + By' = 0$.
14. $2\,x'y' = a^2$.
15. $x'^2 - y'^2 = a^2$.
16. $x'^2 + 2\,y'^2 = 4$.
17. $y'^2 + 8\,x' = 0$.
18. $4\,x'^2 + 25\,y'^2 = 100$.

Pages 66–68. Miscellaneous Exercises

3. (a) $(2, 2)$, $(2, 2)$, $\left(-1 - \sqrt{3},\ -1 + \sqrt{3}\right)$, $\left(-1 + \sqrt{3},\ -1 - \sqrt{3}\right)$.
   (b) $(1, 1)$, $(1, 1)$, $(-3, -1)$. (c) $(2, -1)$, $(5, 5)$, $(5, 5)$. (d) $(0, 1)$, $(3, -2)$,
        $(4, -3)$. (e) $(3, 6)$, $\left(-3, \frac{3}{2}\right)$, $(-5, 0)$. (f) $(1, 0)$, $(1, 0)$, $(3, 2)$.
4. (a) $5\sqrt{2}$, 7. (b) $89°\ 11'$.   12. $x + y = 1$.
7. $A + C = 0$.   23. $V = x^3$, $S = 6\,x^2$, $D = x\sqrt{3}$.
9. $y^2 + 2\,x^3 = 0$.   27. $V = 4\,x^3 - 48\,x^2 + 144\,x$.
11. $x = 2$.   29. $a = x\sqrt{36 - x^2}$ (x is one half the base).

Pages 70–72

1. (a) $x^2 + y^2 = 16$. (c) $x^2 + y^2 - 12\,x - 6\,y = 0$.
   (e) $x^2 + y^2 - 6\,x - 10\,y + 9 = 0$.
2. (a) $x^2 + y^2 - 2\,rx - 2\,ry + r^2 = 0$. (c) $x^2 + y^2 + 2\,rx + 2\,ry + r^2 = 0$.
3. $x^2 + y^2 - 12\,x - 8\,y = 0$.   4. $x^2 + y^2 - 18\,x - 4\,y + 65 = 0$.
5. (a) $(x - 2)^2 + (y - 4)^2 = 16$, center $(2, 4)$, $r = 4$.
   (c) $(x - 4)^2 + y^2 = 9$, center $(4, 0)$, $r = 3$.
   (g) $\left(x - \frac{3}{4}\right)^2 + \left(y + \frac{5}{4}\right)^2 = \frac{29}{8}$, center $\left(\frac{3}{4}, -\frac{5}{4}\right)$, $r = \frac{1}{4}\sqrt{58}$.
   (k) $(x - a)^2 + y^2 = a^2$, center $(a, 0)$, $r = a$.
6. $3\,x - 5\,y = 9$.
8. (a) $x^2 + y^2 = r^2$. (b) $x^2 + y^2 + ax = 0$. (e) $x^2 + y^2 - 2\,hx = 36 - h^2$.
   (f) $x^2 + y^2 - 2\,hx \pm 2\sqrt{25 - h^2}\,y = 0$.
10. $x^2 + y^2 + 5\,x - 6\,y = 28$.   12. $x^2 + y^2 - 10\,x + 6\,y + 25 = 0$.

Pages 74–75

1. (a) $x^2 + y^2 - 5x - y + 4 = 0$. (c) $x^2 + y^2 - 2x - 4y - 5 = 0$.
2. (a) $4x^2 + 4y^2 - 50x - 35y + 115 = 0$.
   (c) $15x^2 + 15y^2 - 52x + 190y - 668 = 0$.
4. $x^2 + y^2 - 12x - 6y = 5$.   6. $x^2 + y^2 - 10x - 8y + 16 = 0$.
5. $x^2 + y^2 - 8x - 12y = 20$.   7. $x^2 + y^2 - 16x + 8y + 60 = 0$.
8. $x^2 + y^2 - 12x + 4 = 0$, $x^2 + y^2 + 20x + 68 = 0$.
9. $x^2 + y^2 + 6x - 8y + 5 = 0$.
10. $x^2 + y^2 - 12x - 18y + 17 = 0$, $x^2 + y^2 + 4x + 14y = 47$.
11. $x^2 + y^2 - 4x - 4y + 4 = 0$, $x^2 + y^2 - 20x - 20y + 100 = 0$.
12. $4x^2 + 4y^2 - 20x - 20y + 25 = 0$, $36x^2 + 36y^2 - 60x + 60y + 25 = 0$.
13. $x^2 + y^2 - 20y = 0$, $x^2 + y^2 - 20x - 10y + 100 = 0$.
14. (a) $x^2 + y^2 - 8x - 2y + 7 = 0$, $x^2 + y^2 - 3x - 7y + 12 = 0$.
    (b) $x^2 + y^2 - 8x - 2y + 7 = 0$. (c) Impossible.
15. $x^2 + y^2 - 4x - 16y + 43 = 0$, $5x^2 + 5y^2 - 12x - 24y + 31 = 0$.
16. $2x^2 + 2y^2 - 4x - 20y - 29 = 0$.
17. $x^2 + y^2 - 22x + 20y + 123 = 0$.

Pages 78–79

1. $2x^2 + 2y^2 - 3x - 14y = 0$.   5. (1) $7x + 2y = 30$. (3) $x + y = 0$.
2. $x^2 + y^2 - 20x + 8y + 31 = 0$.   6. 10.
3. $x^2 + y^2 - 2x + 2y - 16 = 0$.   8. $3x + y - 10 = 0$.
4. (a) $x^2 + y^2 + 9x - 4 = 0$.   11. 10.
   (b) $x^2 + y^2 - 9x - 9y + 5 = 0$.   14. $(1, -\frac{5}{2})$.

Page 79. Miscellaneous Exercises

1. $x^2 + y^2 = 80$, $x^2 + y^2 = 20$.   4. $(2, 3)$.
2. $x^2 + y^2 - 2x - 4y - 15 = 0$.   5. $(7, 1)$, $(-1, 5)$.
3. $3x^2 + 3y^2 - 2a\sqrt{3}\,y - 3a^2 = 0$.   6. $(2, 3)$, $(6, 5)$.
7. $x^2 + y^2 + 10x - 2y - 14 = 0$, $x^2 + y^2 - 14x - 10y + 34 = 0$.
8. $x - 4y + 7 = 0$.   9. $3x - y = \pm 20$.
10. (a) $2x - 3y - 18 = 0$. (b) $3x + 2y = 14$, $3x + 2y + 12 = 0$.
11. $(-4, 0)$, $(16, 0)$.
12. $(mx - 1 \pm \sqrt{1 + m^2})^2 + m^2(y - 1)^2 = m^2$,
    $(mx + 1 \pm \sqrt{1 + m^2})^2 + m^2(y + 1)^2 = m^2$.

Pages 83–85

1. (a) $(1, 0)$, 4, $x + 1 = 0$. (b) $(-\frac{3}{2}, 0)$, 6, $2x = 3$. (c) $(0, 3)$, 12, $y + 3 = 0$.
2. (a) $3y^2 = x$, $x^2 = 9y$. (c) $5y^2 + 8x = 0$, $x^2 = 25y$. (e) $y^2 = 6x$, $x^2 = 6y$.
3. $2p$.   11. $x^2 + y^2 - 10x = 0$.
5. (a) $y^2 + 8x - 16 = 0$.   12. $4p$.
   (c) $x^2 - 2x + 8y + 9 = 0$.   13. 25.
6. $y^2 - 2px + p^2 = 0$.   14. 9 feet.
10. $4x^2 + 4y^2 - 4px - 3p^2 = 0$.   15. 32.5 feet.

Pages 87–88

1. (a) Vertex $(3, 1)$, focus $(5, 1)$, latus rectum 8, directrix $x = 1$, axis $y = 1$.
   (c) Vertex $(2, -6)$, focus $(2, -\frac{11}{2})$, latus rectum 2, directrix $2y + 13 = 0$, axis $x = 2$.
2. (a) $y^2 - 6y - 12x + 21 = 0$.
   (c) $x^2 - 6x - 2y + 10 = 0$.
   (e) $y^2 - 2y - 10x - 24 = 0$.
3. $2x - y + 4 = 0$, $2x + y = 0$.   4. $10\sqrt{2}$.
5. (a) $y^2 - 2y - 3x + 7 = 0$. (b) $x^2 - 4x + 3y + 1 = 0$.
7. (a) x-intercepts 1 and 5, y-intercept 5, axis $x = 3$, vertex $(3, -4)$.
8. (a) $2x^2 - 3x - y - 1 = 0$. (b) $2y^2 - y + 9x - 19 = 0$.
9. Focus $(3, 1)$, directrix $x = 1$.

Page 91

1. (a) Semiaxes 6, 4, foci $(\pm 2\sqrt{5}, 0)$, $e = \frac{\sqrt{5}}{3}$.   4. $x^2 + 3y^2 = 28$.
   (b) Semiaxes 5, 3, foci $(0, \pm 4)$, $e = \frac{4}{5}$.   5. $x^2 + 4y^2 = 36$.
   (c) Semiaxes $2\sqrt{3}$, 2, foci $(\pm 2\sqrt{2}, 0)$, $e = \frac{\sqrt{6}}{3}$. 6. $\frac{2b^2}{a}$.
2. (a) $3x^2 + 4y^2 = 48$.   7. $5y^2 = x$.
   (b) $34x^2 + 25y^2 = 850$.   8. $25x^2 + 9y^2 = 900$.
3. (a) $3x^2 + 4y^2 = 3a^2$.   9. (a) 2.01 feet. (b) 5.08 feet.
   (b) $x^2 + 2y^2 = a^2$.   11. 5 feet 6.6 inches, 4 feet 4.4 inches.

Pages 94–95

1. (a) Center $(-2, 4)$, semiaxes $6\sqrt{2}$, 6, foci $(-8, 4)$, $(4, 4)$.
   (b) Center $(-2, -3)$, semiaxes $2\sqrt{6}$, $2\sqrt{2}$, foci $(-2, -7)$, $(-2, 1)$.
2. (a) $9(x - 4)^2 + 25(y - 2)^2 = 225$.
   (b) $9x^2 + 8y^2 + 18x - 48y - 207 = 0$.
3. $x^2 + y^2 - 20y = 0$.   5. $x^2 + 4y^2 - 4x - 8y - 92 = 0$.
4. $4y^2 + 9x = 0$.   7. $3x^2 + 4y^2 - 18x - 8y - 17 = 0$.
     10. $\frac{1}{2}$.

Pages 98–99

1. (a) Semiaxes 4, 3, $e = \frac{5}{4}$, foci $(\pm 5, 0)$, asymptotes $3x \pm 4y = 0$.
   (b) Semiaxes $2\sqrt{5}$, 4, $e = \frac{3\sqrt{5}}{5}$, foci $(0, \pm 6)$, asymptotes $\sqrt{5}x \pm 2y = 0$.
2. (a) $5x^2 - 4y^2 = 80$. (b) $9x^2 - 40y^2 + 360 = 0$.
3. $3x^2 - y^2 = 3a^2$.   8. $\frac{2b^2}{a}$.
4. $16x^2 - 9y^2 = 576$.
5. $3x^2 - y^2 = 12$.   9. $x^2 + 12y^2 - 16x = 0$.
6. $x^2 - 3y^2 = 6$.   10. $x^2 - 8y^2 + 32 = 0$.
7. $5x^2 - y^2 + 20 = 0$.

ANSWERS

Pages 102–103

1. (a) Center (2, 3), semiaxes $3\sqrt{3}$, 3, foci $(-4, 3)$, $(8, 3)$, asymptotes
$x + \sqrt{3}\, y = 2 + 3\sqrt{3}$, $x - \sqrt{3}\, y = 2 - 3\sqrt{3}$.
   (b) Center $(-3, 4)$, semiaxes 4, 3, foci $(-3, -1)$, $(-3, 9)$, asymptotes
$4\, x + 3\, y = 0$, $4\, x - 3\, y + 24 = 0$.
2. (a) $9(x - 5)^2 - 16(y - 2)^2 = 144$.   (b) $x^2 - 3\, y^2 - 2\, x + 13 = 0$.
3. $x^2 + 4\, y^2 - 12\, x = 0$.
5. Vertices $(4, 4)$, $(-4, -4)$, axes $8\sqrt{2}$, $8\sqrt{2}$, foci $(\pm 4\sqrt{2}, \pm 4\sqrt{2})$.
6. (a) $\frac{1}{16}\, x^2 - \frac{1}{9}\, y^2 = -1$.   9. $8\, x^2 - y^2 - 16\, x + 2\, y - 65 = 0$.
8. $3\, x^2 - 4\, y^2 - 24\, x - 16\, y + 20 = 0$.   12. 3.

Pages 108–109

1. (a) $y^2 - 2\, y - 4\, x + 5 = 0$.
   (b) $4\, x^2 - 4\, xy + y^2 - 8\, x - 16\, y + 24 = 0$.
2. (a) Parabola, $y'^2 = x'$.
   (c) Ellipse, $x'^2 + 2\, y'^2 - x' = 0$.
   (e) Hyperbola, $x'^2 - y'^2 = 9$.
6. $x^2 - 2\, xy + y^2 - 3\, x + 5\, y = 0$.

Pages 109–110. Miscellaneous Exercises

2. (a) Parabola. (b) Ellipse. (c) Hyperbola. (d) Two lines.
3. Ellipse, hyperbola.
5. Vertex $(\frac{1}{4}\, a, \frac{1}{4}\, a)$, focus $(\frac{1}{2}\, a, \frac{1}{2}\, a)$, $x + y = 0$.
6. $(-1, -1)$, $(-1, -1)$, $(5 \pm 2\sqrt{6}, 5 \mp 2\sqrt{6})$.
7. $\left(4 + \dfrac{4\sqrt{5}}{5}, \pm \dfrac{4\sqrt{5}}{5}\right)$, $\left(4 - \dfrac{4\sqrt{5}}{5}, \pm \dfrac{4\sqrt{5}}{5}\right)$.
8. $16\, x^2 + 25\, y^2 = 625$.
11. $b^2 x^2 + a^2 y^2 = ab^2 x$ (if chords are drawn from origin).

Page 121. Miscellaneous Exercises

22. $x = a \log_e \left(\dfrac{y \pm \sqrt{y^2 - a^2}}{a}\right)$.   23. $y = \dfrac{(e^x \pm e^{-x})}{2}$.
24. $(x^2 + y^2 + c^2)^2 - 4\, c^2 x^2 = a^4$ (x-axis through fixed points with origin
midway between them).
25. $(x^2 + y^2)^2 = 2\, a^2(x^2 - y^2)$.
27. $x^2 + y^2 + 20\, x - 8\, y = 0$.
28. $py^2 - 2\, x(x^2 + y^2) = 0$.
29. (a) $b^2(x^2 + y^2)^2 = a^2(b^2 x^2 + a^2 y^2)$.
    (b) $a^2(x^2 + y^2)^2 = b^2(b^2 x^2 + a^2 y^2)$.
30. $b^2(x^2 + y^2)^2 = a^2(b^2 x^2 - a^2 y^2)$.

Pages 125–126

9. $25 x^2 + 16 y^2 = 400.$

10. $16(x - 2)^2 + 9(y + 1)^2 = 144.$

11. $(x - 3)^2 + (y + 1)^2 = 4.$

12. $x^2 + y^2 = 2.$

13. $y = 2 x^2 + 3 x.$

14. Arc of parabola $2 y^2 = 1 - x.$

15. Arc of parabola $2 x^2 = y.$

16. $xy = 4.$

17. $b^2x^2 - a^2y^2 = a^2b^2.$

18. $x^2 - y^2 = 4.$

19. $x^2 + xy = y.$

20. Arc of $y^2 = x^3.$

26. $x = \dfrac{2\,p}{m^2}, \ y = \dfrac{2\,p}{m}.$

27. (a) $x = 3 \cos \pi t, \ y = 3 \sin \pi t.$

    (b) $x = -3 \sin \pi t,$
       $y = 3 \cos \pi t.$

    (c) $x = 3 \cos \pi(t + \frac{1}{4}),$
       $y = 3 \sin \pi(t + \frac{1}{4}).$
       (t is time in seconds.)

28. $x = v_0 t, \ y = -\frac{1}{2} g t^2.$

29. 69,282 feet, 10,000 feet.

30. 1,385.6 feet, or 67,896.4 feet.

31. 120 feet per second.

Page 128

2. $20\,\pi$, 20.

3. $x = a(\theta - \sin \theta), \ y = a(\cos \theta - 1).$

Page 130

5. $\left(\dfrac{5}{2}, \ \dfrac{\pm 5\sqrt{3}}{2} \right)$, $(-5, 0)$ (each point a point of tangency).

Pages 131–132. Miscellaneous Exercises

1. Arc of parabola $2 x^2 = y.$

2. $x^2 - y^2 = x^2y^2.$

3. $x^2y = 3.$

4. $y^2 = x^2 \tan^2 \sqrt{x^2 + y^2}.$

5. $y = x \tan \log_e \sqrt{x^2 + y^2}.$

6. $y^2 - x^2 = 4 x^2y^2.$

7. $x^3 + y^3 = 3 axy.$

8. Arc of parabola $3 x^2 + 2 y = 6.$

9. $(x^2 + y^2)^2 - 6(x^2 + y^2) + 8 x - 3 = 0.$

10. $(x^2 + y^2)^2 = 4 ax^2y.$

11. $\left(\dfrac{x}{a} \right)^2 + \left(\dfrac{y}{b} \right)^{\frac{2}{3}} = 1.$

12. Arc of $y = 8 x^4 - 8 x^2 + 1.$

20. $x = OA\,(\cos kt + \cos 2\,kt), \ y = OA\,(\sin kt + \sin 2\,kt).$

21. $x = \pm\,a \sin \theta, \ y = a \tan \theta(1 \mp \sin \theta)$ (origin at O, MN is x-axis, A is $(a, 0)$, θ is angle OAP).

22. $x = a \cot \theta, \ y = a \sin^2 \theta$ (θ is angle OD makes with positive x-axis).

24. $P: x = 2 \cos kt, y = 2 \sin kt.$ $Q: x = 2(\cos kt + \sqrt{\cos^2 kt + 8}), y = 0.$

25. $x = OQ \cos k_1 t + OQ' \cos k_2 t, \ y = OQ \sin k_1 t + OQ' \sin k_2 t.$

Pages 134–135

3. $(4, 0)$, $\left(4, \dfrac{\pi}{3} \right)$, $\left(4, \dfrac{2\,\pi}{3} \right)$, $(4, \pi)$, $\left(4, \dfrac{4\,\pi}{3} \right)$, $\left(4, \dfrac{5\,\pi}{3} \right)$.

4. $\left(-1, \dfrac{4\,\pi}{3} \right)$, $\left(1, -\dfrac{5\,\pi}{3} \right)$, $\left(-1, -\dfrac{2\,\pi}{3} \right)$.

8. 7.

10. (a) 30. (b) $18\sqrt{3}$. (c) $26\sqrt{3}$. (d) $\dfrac{35\sqrt{3}}{2}$.

Page 137

24. $x^3 = 4\,y.$

25. $x^3 = 2\,y^2.$

26. $xy = 1.$

27. $y^2 = 2\,x + 1.$

28. $3\,x^2 + 4\,y^2 - 2\,x = 1.$

29. $xy = x + y.$

30. $\rho = 10\cos\theta.$

31. $\rho + 10\sin\theta = 0.$

32. $\rho\cos 2\,\theta = 10\cos\theta.$

33. $\rho^2\cos^4\theta = 1.$

Pages 140–141

5. (a) $x = 3.$ (b) $y + 1 = 0.$ (c) $y = \sqrt{3}\,x.$ (d) $4\,y = 3\,x.$ (e) $x + y = 4.$
(f) $x - \sqrt{3}\,y + 6 = 0.$

6. $\theta = 0,\ \rho\cos\theta = 5,\ \theta = \dfrac{\pi}{2},\ \rho\sin\theta = 5;\ \theta = \dfrac{\pi}{4},\ 2\,\rho\cos\left(\theta - \dfrac{\pi}{4}\right) = 5\sqrt{2}.$

12. $\rho = \dfrac{ep}{1 + e\cos\theta}$ (pole at focus).

13. $\rho = \dfrac{ep}{1 + e\sin\theta},\ \rho = \dfrac{ep}{1 - e\sin\theta}.$

17. $\rho = 2\,p\cot\theta\csc\theta.$

18. $\rho^2(a^2\sin^2\theta + b^2\cos^2\theta) = a^2b^2.$

19. $\rho^2(b^2\cos^2\theta - a^2\sin^2\theta) = a^2b^2.$

Page 144

25. $y = x\tan\dfrac{a}{\sqrt{x^2 + y^2}}.$

26. $(x^2 + y^2)^3 = a^2(x^2 - y^2)^2.$

27. $(x^2 + y^2 + ay)^2 = a^2(x^2 + y^2).$

28. $\rho = a\theta.$

Page 145

1. $\left(6,\ \pm\dfrac{\pi}{3}\right).$

3. $\left(3,\ \pm\dfrac{\pi}{3}\right),\ \left(3,\ \pm\dfrac{2\,\pi}{3}\right).$

5. $(a, 1),\ (-a, -1),$ and an infinite number of other intersections.

7. $(0, 0),\ (a, 1).$

9. $\left(\dfrac{a\sqrt{3}}{2},\ 10°\right),\quad \left(\dfrac{-a\sqrt{3}}{2},\ 50°\right),\quad \left(\dfrac{a\sqrt{3}}{2},\ 130°\right),\quad \left(\dfrac{-a\sqrt{3}}{2},\ 170°\right),$
$\left(\dfrac{a\sqrt{3}}{2},\ 250°\right),\ \left(\dfrac{-a\sqrt{3}}{2},\ 290°\right),$ and at the pole.

11. $\left(2\sqrt{2},\ \dfrac{\pi}{4}\right),$ and at the pole.

13. $\left(\dfrac{a}{2},\ \pm\dfrac{\pi}{3}\right),$ and at the pole.

15. $\left(4,\ \dfrac{\pi}{2}\right),\ (-\tfrac{12}{5},\ 216°\ 52'),$ and at the pole.

17. $(0, 0),\ \left(a,\ \dfrac{3\,\pi}{2}\right),$ and four other intersections.

18. $\left(a,\ \dfrac{\pi}{2}\right),\ \left(a,\ \dfrac{\pi}{2}\right),\ \left(a,\ -\dfrac{\pi}{2}\right),\ \left(a,\ -\dfrac{\pi}{2}\right).$

Pages 146–147. Miscellaneous Exercises

4. $\rho^2 = \sec\theta(\csc\theta - a^2 \sec\theta)$.

5. $\rho = \sec\theta(2 - \tan^3\theta)$.

6. $\rho = -4\cos 2\theta \sec^3\theta$.

7. $\rho = 2\cos 3\theta$.

8. $\rho^2 = \tan^2\theta$.

9. $a^2\rho^2 = \csc^2 4\theta$.

12. $\rho = 2a\sin\theta\tan\theta$.

15. $\rho = a\sec\theta \pm b$.

16. $\rho^2 = 2a^2\cos 2\theta$.

21. $\rho = a\left(3 - 4\sin^2\dfrac{\theta}{2}\right)$.

Page 153

1. (a) 6, direction cosines $\frac{2}{3}, \frac{2}{3}, \frac{1}{3}$. (e) 5, direction cosines 0, 1, 0.

2. (a) 7, direction cosines $\frac{6}{7}, \frac{3}{7}, -\frac{2}{7}$. (f) 10, direction cosines 1, 0, 0.

3. (a) $\gamma = 45°, 135°$. (b) Impossible.

5. $54°\,44'$.

6. (a) $\frac{1}{3}, \frac{2}{3}, \frac{2}{3}$. (d) $\dfrac{\sqrt{2}}{2}, \dfrac{\sqrt{2}}{2}, 0$.

8. $(0, 0, 0)$, $(4, 0, 0)$.

9. $y^2 + z^2 - 6y - 12z = 0$.

10. $x^2 + y^2 + z^2 - 4x - 6y - 12z = 0$.

11. $36°\,52'$.

12. $64°\,54'$.

Pages 158–159

2. (a) 2. (b) $\sqrt{3}$.

7. $3x - 2y = 0$.

8. $5y + 3z = 15$.

9. $2x + z = 13$.

10. $x + 2y + 3z = 8$.

11. $3x + y - 4z = 0$.

12. $x + y - z = 0$.

13. $4y - z = 3$.

15. (a) $\dfrac{\sqrt{14}}{7}, \dfrac{-\sqrt{14}}{14}, \dfrac{3\sqrt{14}}{14}$.

(c) $\frac{4}{5}, -\frac{3}{5}, 0$.

16. $3x + 6y + 2z = 49$.

17. $x - 4y + 3z + 1 = 0$.

18. $x - 3y + 2z = 11$.

21. $60°$.

22. $54°\,44'$.

23. (a) $a_1a_2 + b_1b_2 + c_1c_2 = 0$.

(b) $\dfrac{a_1}{a_2} = \dfrac{b_1}{b_2} = \dfrac{c_1}{c_2}$.

(c) $\dfrac{a_1}{a_2} = \dfrac{b_1}{b_2} = \dfrac{c_1}{c_2} = \dfrac{d_1}{d_2}$.

24. $\frac{3}{2}$.

26. $(2, -1, 6)$.

28. $(8, 4, 1)$.

Pages 163–164

1. (a) $5x + 4y = 34$,
$3y + 5z = 8$,
$3x - 4z = 14$.

2. (a) $(\frac{14}{3}, \frac{8}{3}, 0), (\frac{34}{5}, 0, \frac{8}{5}), (0, \frac{17}{2}, -\frac{7}{2})$.

3. (a) $\dfrac{x-6}{8} = \dfrac{y-2}{4} = \dfrac{z-4}{1}$.

(b) $\dfrac{x+1}{6} = \dfrac{y-3}{-3} = \dfrac{z+2}{2}$.

(e) $\dfrac{x-3}{4} = \dfrac{y-2}{3}, z = 0$.

4. $\dfrac{x-2}{11} = \dfrac{y-6}{2} = \dfrac{z-1}{10}$.

5. $x = y = z$.

8. $\dfrac{x-5}{2} = \dfrac{y-4}{3} = \dfrac{z-8}{6}$.

9. $(-2, 1, 0)$.

10. $\dfrac{5\sqrt{5}}{2}$.

11. $(3, 5, 3)$.

12. (a) $\dfrac{x}{6} = \dfrac{y-\frac{7}{2}}{3} = \dfrac{z+\frac{7}{3}}{2}$.

13. (a) $\frac{1}{3}, \frac{2}{3}, \frac{2}{3}$.

14. $\dfrac{x+5}{7} = \dfrac{y-2}{4} = \dfrac{z+3}{4}$.

Pages 164-165. Miscellaneous Exercises

1. $x + 2z = 9.$
2. $3x + 5y - z + 5 = 0.$
3. $(\frac{5}{3}, \frac{5}{3}, \frac{16}{3}).$
6. $5x + y + z = 7.$
7. $4x - y + 2z = 11.$
9. (a) 4. (b) $-\frac{1}{3}$. (c) 0.
10. 5.
11. $2\sqrt{6}.$

12. $30°.$
13. $x + 4y + 2z = 1.$
14. $5x - 7y - 4z + 59 = 0.$
15. $\dfrac{x-6}{2} = \dfrac{y-4}{2} = \dfrac{z-1}{1},$

$\qquad \dfrac{x-6}{34} = \dfrac{y-4}{-38} = \dfrac{z-1}{-1}.$

Page 167

15. $y^2 = 8x - 16.$

16. $16x^2 + 25y^2 - 96x - 256 = 0.$

Pages 168-169

1. (a) $z^2 + y^2 = 4x.$ (b) $9x^2 + 25y^2 + 25z^2 = 225.$
   (c) $x^2 + y^2 - (4 - z)^2 = 0.$ (d) $4x^2 + 4z^2 - 9y^2 = 0.$
   (e) (1) $b^2x^2 - a^2y^2 - a^2z^2 = a^2b^2,$ (2) $b^2x^2 + b^2z^2 - a^2y^2 = a^2b^2.$
   (f) $y^2 + z^2 = \sin^2 x.$
3. $y^2 + z^2 - 2ax + a^2 = 0.$
4. $\dfrac{x^2}{64} + \dfrac{y^2}{64} + \dfrac{z^2}{289} = 1.$

13. $9x^2 - 16(y - 3)^2 + 9z^2 = 0.$
14. $(x^2 + y^2 + z^2 - a^2 + b^2)^2 = 4b^2(y^2 + z^2).$

Pages 177-178

The projections are given in the order xy-plane, yz-plane, xz-plane.
1. Points $(3, \pm\sqrt{7})$, lines $y = \pm\sqrt{7}$, line $x = 3.$
2. Circle $x^2 + y^2 = 16$, line $z = 4$, line $z = 4.$
3. Circle $x^2 + y^2 = 16$, circle $y^2 + z^2 - 10z + 9 = 0$, line $x + z = 5.$
5. Line $y = 4$, line $y = 4$, circle $x^2 + z^2 = 48.$
6. Line $y = \sqrt{3}x$, ellipse $4y^2 + 3z^2 = 192$, ellipse $4x^2 + z^2 = 64.$
8. Lines $x = \pm 4$, circle $y^2 + z^2 = 48$, lines $x = \pm 4.$
9. Points $(2, \pm 2\sqrt{2})$, lines $y = \pm 2\sqrt{2}$, line $x = 2.$
11. Parabola $y^2 = 4 - x$, parabola $y^2 = 4 - z$, line $z = x.$
12. Parabola $y = x^2$, parabola $z^2 = 1 - y$, circle $x^2 + z^2 = 1.$
13. Circle, ellipse, line.
14. Line $x - y = 4$, circle $y^2 + z^2 - 2y = 8$, circle $x^2 + z^2 - 10x + 16 = 0.$
15. Line, ellipse, circle.
16. Line, parabola, parabola.
17. $x^2 + y^2 - 4x = 0$, $z^4 - 16z^2 + 16y^2 = 0$, $z^2 + 4x = 16.$
18. Ellipse, ellipse, ellipse.
20. Ellipse, ellipse, line.
22. Circle, line, circle.

Page 180

1. (a) In rectangular coördinates $(2\sqrt{6}, 2\sqrt{6}, 4)$, in cylindrical coördinates $\left(4\sqrt{3}, \dfrac{\pi}{4}, 4\right)$.

2. (a) In rectangular coördinates $\left(\dfrac{5\sqrt{3}}{2}, \dfrac{5}{2}, 6\right)$, in spherical coördinates $\left(\sqrt{61}, \dfrac{\pi}{6}, \tan^{-1}\dfrac{5}{6}\right)$.

3. (a) In cylindrical coördinates $(3\sqrt{5}, \tan^{-1}\tfrac{1}{2}, 0)$, in spherical coördinates $\left(3\sqrt{5}, \tan^{-1}\dfrac{1}{2}, \dfrac{\pi}{2}\right)$.

4. (a) $r^2 = 5z$. (b) $z = a\tan\theta$ (cylindrical), $\rho = a\tan\theta\sec\phi$ (spherical).

5. (a) $(x^2 + y^2 + z^2)(x^2 + y^2) = 6xyz$. (c) $x^2 + y^2 - (z - a)^2 = 0$.

Page 181. Miscellaneous Exercises

2. $(x - 3)^2 + (y - 4)^2 = 25$.

3. $x^2 + y^2 + z^2 - 14x = 0$.

4. $5x - y - 4z - 53 = 0$.

5. $(2, 4, 0), (0, 2, 1)$.

6. $x^2(y^2 + z^2) = a^4$ (about x-axis)

9. $x^2 - y^2 - (z - 2)^2 = 0$.

10. $16p^2(x - p)^2 + 16p^2z^2 - (4p^2 - y^2)^2 = 0$.

INDEX

PRINTED IN THE UNITED STATES OF AMERICA